CU00766219

Mtetezi

Developing mental health advocacy with African and Caribbean men

Karen Newbigging, Mick McKeown, Evette A. Hunkins-Hutchinson
and Dr Beverley French

With Zemikael Habte-Mariam, Linda Coleman-Hill, Dennis Mullings,
Anthony Stephens and Keith Holt

First published in Great Britain in June 2007
by the Social Care Institute for Excellence

ISBN 978-1-904812-39-5

Written by Karen Newbigging, Mick McKeown, Evette A. Hunkins-
Hutchinson and Dr Beverley French
With Zemikael Habte-Mariam, Linda Coleman-Hill, Dennis Mullings,
Anthony Stephens and Keith Holt

This report is available online
www.scie.org.uk

Social Care Institute for Excellence
Goldings House
2 Hay's Lane
London SE1 2HB
tel 020 7089 6840
fax 020 7089 6841
textphone 020 7089 6893
www.scie.org.uk

Front cover images produced by Susan Rentoul Design

Give a man a fish and you feed him for a day.
Teach a man to fish and you feed him for life.*

*See acknowledgements on page vii

Acknowledgements

We are deeply grateful to the many individuals and organisations that actively supported this work. We are grateful to members of the Project Steering Group for their time and invaluable comments. Above all we would like to thank all of the men who took part in the focus groups and interviews, who breathed life into our work. We would also like to thank those other individuals and organisations that have given freely of their time and advice. We thank you all.

Project Steering Group members: Dr Di Barnes, Zemikael Habte-Mariam (Chair), Evette Hunkins-Hutchinson, Philip Jones (from 1.8.06), Karen Mellanby, Professor Kwame McKenzie, Dennis Mullings, Karen Newbigging, Danny Sollé (until 31.7.06), Anthony Stephens, Dominic Makuvachuma Walker (until 31.03.06) and Bernadette Ward (until 31.7.06).

The title of this review and proverb in the opening pages were identified by the partner organisations. Mtetezi is a Swahili word and refers to a person who advocates and champions an individual's rights. Utetezi is a similar word and refers to the process of advocacy. We are grateful to Evette Hunkins-Hutchinson and Kipnyango Seroney for their help in defining these terms. The proverb captures the essence of advocacy and that is self-empowerment.

Individuals

Gloria Browne, Diverse Minds
Dawn Bryan, African Caribbean Mental Health Service Manchester
Julie Jaye Charles, Equalities National Council for Disabled People and
    Carers from Black and Minority Ethnic Communities
Michael Coleman-Hill
Dr Clare Collins, Centre for Ethnicity and Health, UCLAN
Richard Greenall, Department of Nursing, UCLAN
Professor Chris Heginbotham, Centre for Ethnicity and Health, UCLAN and Mental Health Act Commission
Tunde Ife, CSIP West Midlands
Eileen Jackson, Centre for Ethnicity and Health, UCLAN

Margaret Kumbuka, SOAS Language Centre, University of London

Dr Timothy Lister

Linda Newton, Cardiff and Vale Mental Health Development Project

Sadie Palmer, SACMHA

Dr Roiyah Saltus, University of Glamorgan

Lisa Shoja, Comensus Project (community engagement and service user and carer support), UCLAN

Laura Salisbury, Centre for Ethnicity and Health, UCLAN

Angela Simpson, Black and Asian Mental Health Research Project (BAMHRP), Derby

Suzanne Smith, AWETU, Cardiff

Val Snape, Lancashire Advocacy

Dominic Makuvachuma Walker, Catch-A-Fiya

Organisations

ACCI (African Caribbean Community Initiative), Wolverhampton

Action 4 Advocacy

Advocacy in Barnet

Advocacy Matters, Warrington

Advocacy Northants

African and African Caribbean Advocacy Project, Haringuey, North London

African and Caribbean Mental Health Services, Manchester

Age Concern Advocacy Project, Coventry

Akwaaba Ayeh Project, Leicester

Assert, Kent

Assist (Advocacy Services in Staffordshire)

AWETU, Cardiff

Black and Asian Mental Health Research Project

Black and Ethnic Community Partnership, Brighton & Hove

Black Health Agency, Manchester

Black Orchid (Bristol Black Mental Health Advocacy Project)

Black People's Mental Health Association, London

Blackpool, Fylde and Wyre Mind

Boys 2 Men

Brent Advocacy Concerns

Bromley Advocacy

Community Services Network, London
Congolese Action Group
Dignity, Luton
Dorset Mental Health Advocacy
East Lancs Advocacy
Equalities, National Council for Black and Disabled People
Ethiopian Community in Lambeth
Fanon Resource Centre, London
Freshwinds Unity Trust, Birmingham
Friends and Advocates
Gloucester Black Mental Health Services
James Wiltshire Trust, Southampton
Kent Multi-cultural Community Association
Kingston Advocacy Group
Kuumba Centre, Sandwell African Caribbean Mental Health
   Foundation, Birmingham
Lancashire Advocacy
Leeds Crisis Centre
Leeds Mental Health Advocacy Group
London Cyrenians Housing
Loud and Clear Mental Health Advocacy
Millennium Centre, Derby
Mind in Camden Community Advocacy Service
Mind in Havant Advocacy Service
Oremi, London
Pages Advocacy, Plymouth
Pettigift, African Centred Mental Health Care, Birmingham
Rethink, Northern Ireland
Sandwell African Caribbean Mental Health Foundation
Sharing Voices, Bradford
Sheffield African and Caribbean Mental Health Association
Solent Mind
South London Congolese Association
South Wales Mental Health Advocacy
Southside Partnership, London
Sutton Advocacy for Mental Health
The Advocacy Project, Toxteth, Liverpool

The Civis Trust
Touchstone, Leeds
Unity Group, Southampton
Walthamstow Black Mental Health Users Group
West Indian Families Association
Yes Africa

List of abbreviations

ACMHS	African and Caribbean Mental Health Service
BVCS	Black voluntary and community sector
BME	Black and minority ethnic
CDW	Community development worker
CPA	Care programme approach
DH	Department of Health
HCC	Healthcare Commission
IMCA	Independent mental capacity advocate
LA	Lancashire Advocacy
NSF	National Service Framework
PCT	Primary care trust
smi	Serious mental illness
SCIE	Social Care Institute for Excellence
SCMH	Sainsbury Centre for Mental Health
UCLAN	University of Central Lancashire
WHO	World Health Organisation

Potential conflicts of interest

The three partner organisations are all involved in the provision of mental health advocacy services and two, the African and Caribbean Mental Health Service (ACMHS) and Equalities, specifically to African and Caribbean communities. There are no conflicts of interest for the principal investigator, Karen Newbigging, or Dr Beverley French and Evette Hunkins-Hutchinson. Mick McKeown is the author of one of the papers in the in-depth analysis and was a member of the Steering Group for the development of Mind's service user standards for advocacy.[1] He was therefore not involved in reviewing these papers.

A note on terminology

Many of the terms used in this report are contested. We have sought to use terms that are accurate and widely understood, while recognising that other terminology may be preferred. Our experience indicates that the struggle for language needs to continue, and that accepted meanings associated with specific terminology can change over time.

We have used the term 'African and Caribbean' to refer to people of African and/or Caribbean origin inclusive of Black African, Black Caribbean, White/Black Caribbean Mixed and White/Black African. We have used this in preference to the term 'African Caribbean' as it more accurately reflects the heterogeneity of these communities.[2]

The term Black and minority ethnic (BME) is used to refer to a range of diverse communities, including African and Caribbean communities.

We rely on the term 'mental health' throughout. We acknowledge that the term 'mental' may not be widely used or preferred within African and Caribbean communities, and has some pejorative or stigmatising connotations. We considered alternatives, such as emotional health, but opted for mental health – first because it is common currency and second to ensure that it was clear that we are concerned with advocacy for those with serious and persisting needs as well as those with more transient mental health issues.

We have used the term 'service user' to describe people with mental health problems who are using mental health services but understand that many would prefer to be described as 'survivors'.

A broad range of meanings of advocacy is explored within this report. We have used the term 'professional advocacy' to refer to paid workers who are trained to deliver advocacy. This is not meant to imply that advocacy provided by volunteers or community members is any less useful. A fuller description of the different definitions of advocacy is provided in Appendix 5. The Knowledge Review discusses four main types of advocacy: *generic advocacy*, covering a range of people as well as those with mental health problems; *mental health advocacy* to cover all forms of mental health advocacy; *BME mental health advocacy* to cover mental health advocacy to a diverse range of BME communities, including

African and Caribbean communities; and *African and Caribbean mental health advocacy* to cover mental health advocacy specifically for African and Caribbean communities. The terms 'client' or 'partner' have been used to describe someone using advocacy, in whatever form.

Executive summary

The Knowledge Review had two elements:

- A Research Review, to establish what was already known about the provision of mental health advocacy with African and Caribbean men from research reports and service descriptions.
- A Practice Survey, to establish what is currently being provided and what is needed. This involved an e-mail and telephone survey of organisations that might be providing mental health advocacy with African and Caribbean men, focus groups with African and Caribbean men and case studies in two different localities.

The review was undertaken by a project team that included service users, people from African and Caribbean communities, advocacy services and research staff from the University of Central Lancashire (UCLAN).

Research into advocacy for African and Caribbean men

The Research Review indicated a significant gap in high quality evidence of both effectiveness and process evaluation of mental health advocacy for African and Caribbean men. The review therefore drew heavily on service descriptions or accounts of specific initiatives.

Need for advocacy

There is a substantial body of evidence pointing to a negative relationship between mental health services and African and Caribbean men, who are under-represented as users of enabling services and over-represented in the population of patients who are admitted to, compulsorily detained in, and treated by mental health services. The consequences of this are poor engagement with mainstream services, restricted choices and high levels of dissatisfaction with mainstream care. The review identified the potential of advocacy to address these issues and to secure access to the most appropriate forms of support.

Provision of advocacy

Serious gaps in advocacy provision for BME communities were high-lighted by studies focusing on mental health advocacy. It is apparent from both service descriptions and studies of African and Caribbean mental health services that advocacy is provided as part of a wider role. This interdependence with other aspects of provision is viewed as promoting greater opportunities for recovery and well-being. These services have typically developed in response to community needs because of concerns about the inaccessibility and inappropriateness of mainstream mental health services for African and Caribbean and/or BME communities. However, the approach to advocacy of these organisations appears to be qualitatively different and consistent with notions of recovery and social inclusion. The lack of sustainable funding and a preference for a different conception of professional advocacy places such services in jeopardy.

All studies drew attention to the importance of cultural sensitivity and shared heritage had a stronger emphasis in studies focused on BME communities. The service descriptions of mental health advocacy serv-ices referred to cultural sensitivity but rarely elaborated what this means. However, African and Caribbean and BME services articulated this and made a strong argument for the provision of mental health advocacy by independent community organisations that understand this and the disadvantage faced by African and Caribbean men.

Impact of advocacy

There was limited information about the impact of advocacy but its potential in terms of securing basic rights, creating choices, facilitating involvement in decision making and improving access to complementary way of healing and practical support were highlighted.

Features of good practice in the provision of advocacy with African and Caribbean men

These included:

- advocacy that addresses the double discrimination of racism and men-tal illness;

- the provision of a safe and secure relationship within which the feelings of isolation and consequences of stigma associated with mental illness and racism can be addressed;
- the ability to respond to the linguistic and cultural needs of African and Caribbean men, underpinned by an approach that emphasises promotion of health, reintegration of the self, spirituality, self-knowledge and connection to the community;
- choice, especially in terms of gender, and demonstrable ethnic sensitivity;
- a proactive approach to personal advocacy through community-based action and engagement;
- balancing accessibility and informality with professionalism to ensure that advocacy services are delivered to high standards;
- a well-trained, well-equipped and well-supported workforce;
- partnership working and facilitated networking across organisations to encourage cross-referrals, exchange of information, best practice and mutual understanding;
- adequate long-term core funding.

Practice Survey 1: email and telephone survey

This survey aimed to establish the range of mental health advocacy that can be accessed by African and Caribbean men. It involved the development of a database of nearly 400 projects, an email survey and a telephone survey of a sample of 52 organisations.

Current provision

Three broad organisational forms were identified:

- African and Caribbean-focused organisations: geared to meet the needs of African and Caribbean communities;
- BME-focused organisations: designed to meet the needs of diverse BME communities;
- advocacy-focused organisations: stand-alone services oriented to casework advocacy usually referred to as independent professional advocacy.

The survey confirmed that mental health advocacy for African and Caribbean men is most often provided as part of African and Caribbean or BME mental health services, providing a range of other services. They are rooted in the community and therefore understand the importance of Black history, of religious and spiritual beliefs, and of the social problems, in particular racism, faced by African and Caribbean people. Black advocates often voiced their objective as Black empowerment, which intrinsically and inevitably involves challenging mainstream practice.

Mainstream mental health advocacy services start from a different position and emphasise the importance of independent advocacy, often as a distinct service, provided by trained staff. Often this advocacy is short-term and focused on trying to change the relationship between mental health services and a particular service user to ensure they have the sort of help provided in a way that they want. These organisations often do not proactively seek clients, thus disadvantaging African and Caribbean men and members of other BME communities who may find them difficult to access.

While the ideal for advocacy is to achieve empowerment of the individual, in practice, substantial advocacy activity was led by the advocate and approximates to a representational form of advocacy. The location of advocacy therefore becomes important in terms of the extent to which it will facilitate access to other activities that enable personal development and empowerment and are designed to tackle the underlying causes of disadvantage.

Capacity to deliver the range of advocacy is a key issue. The culturally sensitive provision, African and Caribbean or BME-focused, usually had one or two members of staff to deliver advocacy or it was part of a wider role. This raises questions about the capacity of these organisations to deliver the range of advocacy required. The advocacy-focused organisations were generally relatively well staffed, advocacy was their sole business, but, with notable exceptions did not have the capacity to deliver culturally sensitive advocacy.

Access to mental health advocacy by African and Caribbean men

Many organisations did not formally monitor the ethnicity or gender of their clients and therefore data on uptake of advocacy by African and Caribbean men was limited. Where mental health advocacy is provided by an African and Caribbean-focused organisation, more or less all of its client group will be African and Caribbean. Advocacy-focused and BME organisations have varying proportions of clientele drawn from African and Caribbean communities, reflecting in part the local demography or local provision. It would appear that African and Caribbean men make relatively reasonable use of broader BME organisations. The use of generic advocacy and mental health advocacy services by African and Caribbean men, however, tends to be low, but there are substantial variations in usage across these services, in part reflecting demographic variations, with a proportion of inner-city services reporting higher usage. There was scant evidence that mainstream mental heath services are actively facilitating access to advocacy for African and Caribbean service users.

Advocacy outcomes

There was consensus that advocacy could enable African and Caribbean men to get heard and have their needs met more appropriately by having a greater say and greater control, particularly in the relationship with mental health services, and therefore more capacity to determine what treatment and support they received. The outcomes advocacy could deliver often related to the personal goals of an individual but in general included:

- greater range of relationships;
- increased involvement in care planning and ward rounds;
- increased choices and access to a greater range of culturally appropriate care, delivered more consistently and to a higher standard;
- diversion from restrictive forms of care;
- negotiated changes in treatment, particularly a reduction in medication;
- greater independence from mental health services;
- successful resolution of complaints;
- positive changes in staff attitudes;
- increased acceptance and awareness of mental health issues by families and communities;
- more community support activated to ensure greater access to a broad range of social opportunities.

The evidence for the impact of advocacy on any of these was weak. Information about outcomes was largely aspirational or anecdotal with organisations citing capacity as the major barrier to routine data collection. Across the different organisations empowerment and the goal of self-advocacy were identified as key outcomes. However, Black and voluntary community sector (BVCS) organisations went further and identified tackling social disadvantage, including racism, as a key outcome.

Preferred characteristics of advocacy services for African and Caribbean men

These included:

- Cultural sensitivity. For African and Caribbean organisations, this usually meant shared cultural heritage. The articulation of what this means by generic mental health advocacy services was largely underdeveloped, suggesting either a lack of understanding of what this means, how to achieve it or that it is a low priority.
- Facilitating choice both of type of advocacy and advocate.
- Independence from statutory sector provision was stressed by all organisations but the African and Caribbean and BME organisations emphasised the value of interdependence with other voluntary services, facilitating access to advocacy and the potential for a holistic response to a broad range of social needs enabling men to move beyond a relationship with mental health services.
- Strategies to increase accessibility – outreach strategies, location and identity of advocacy provision, provision of advocacy alongside other activities and sensitive timing of advocacy interventions all facilitate access.
- Sustainable funding enabling long-term relationships and community-based advocacy as well as advocacy in in-patient settings and outreach to prison.

Factors that facilitate development of advocacy for African and Caribbean men

These included:

- understanding of cultural identity and context of negative experiences of mental health services;
- understanding of the range of advocacy and its potential;
- sustainable funding;
- availability of organisations positioned and with the capacity to provide advocacy with BME groups;
- effective leadership and management;
- collective advocacy and service user involvement;
- partnerships between organisations.

Practice Survey 2: focus groups and interviews

Four focus groups and a small number of individual interviews were undertaken, involving 30 men in total.

Meaning of advocacy

The term 'advocacy' does not immediately have meaning for African and Caribbean men but is welcomed once there is an appreciation of what it is. This may have implications for access to advocacy and participants had limited experience of advocacy.

Need for advocacy

There was agreement about the need for advocacy and its role in addressing the following issues was identified:

- negative experiences of medication;
- lack of involvement in decision making;
- lack of access to alternative treatments, particularly talking therapies;

- physical confrontations and misinterpretation of behaviour by mental health services reflecting stereotyped attitudes towards African and Caribbean men;
- limited opportunities to have personal experience valued;
- limited opportunities of engagement with community peers and activities;
- involvement of the police and courts in admission;
- greater likelihood of detention and lengthier admission periods.

Characteristics of advocates

The men identified the following:

- shared cultural heritage – the importance of roots in the community and Black identity serve to build confidence in the ability of the advocate and service to accurately listen, understand and act on the men's behalf;
- choice of gender – particularly access to a male advocate;
- personal characteristics – the ability to listen and form a connection and demonstrate commitment to an individual;
- competence – advocates need to 'know what they are doing', understand mental health, what services are available and the needs and context for African and Caribbean men.

Practice Survey 3: case studies

Two case studies, and additional interviews with other stakeholders, were undertaken to establish a more in-depth understanding of the commissioning and provision of advocacy with African and Caribbean men. They confirmed and elaborated the findings from the other elements of the Practice Survey. In addition they highlighted a significant gap with regard to comprehensive and informed arrangements for commissioning advocacy.

Conclusions

While the potential of advocacy for African and Caribbean men is recognised, access is limited with scant evidence of developments in advocacy-focused organisations to engage with this client group. Overlain on this is a mistrust of established mental health services and confusion over the meaning of advocacy, which gets in the way of realising its value and potential benefits.

There is a consensus that African and Caribbean men require advocacy that is culturally sensitive, addresses their experiences of negative interactions with mental health services and facilitates recovery and social inclusion. The evidence on whether mental health advocacy should be provided by a generic BME or an African and Caribbean organisation predominantly reflected the ethnic affiliation of respondents but also demographic considerations. The review considered the advantages and disadvantages of the three different organisational arrangements and found that in general there was a trade-off between cultural sensitivity and appropriateness and the staff resources available to deliver advocacy.

Further, the review indicated a profound difference in advocacy from that of advocacy on behalf of the majority ethnic group. For African and Caribbean men both culturally specific issues and the context of negative experiences and consequent suspicion of mental health services means that advocates will need to ensure that staff are thoroughly informed and may encounter additional resistance from services. It has also raised questions about the role of mental health services in promoting access to mental health advocacy for African and Caribbean men, and indeed for African and Caribbean women and people from other BME communities.

Delivering race equality identified the development of mental health advocacy for BME communities as a key action for primary care trusts (PCTs). This review indicates first, that a strategic approach to the development of a whole system of advocacy provision is needed. This entails understanding the diversity of needs within African and Caribbean communities, including those of women and newly arrived communities, notably refugees and asylum seekers, as well as established communities. Transparency, clarity about decision making and the engagement of communities in this process are essential. Second, it implies reframing what advocacy means to include holistic and collective definitions of advocacy, as have developed within the BVCS. It is important that this model is not disadvantaged or dismissed in any future moves to formalise advocacy and the development of more systematic commissioning arrangements. Third, it requires investment in the capacity of the BVCS to deliver mental health advocacy alongside investment in organisations to support their development. The economic costs of providing inaccessible and inappropriate mental healthcare and the potential for recommissioning need to be explored and realised.

The approach and philosophy of BCVS organisations means that advocacy rooted within these organisations is potentially aligned with current models of recovery. This means that advocacy provided by these organisations has the potential not only to ensure the delivery of more appropriate care and achieve the goal of individual empowerment but also to contribute to tackling underlying social disadvantage and inequalities faced by African and Caribbean men.

1

Research review

1.1   Introduction

There has been increasing concern about the quality of mental healthcare for people from Black and minority ethnic (BME) communities[3,4] and there is now a considerable body of evidence that highlights the negative and discriminatory experiences of these communities. Research has shown that African and Caribbean men comprise a social group that experience particular difficulty accessing appropriate mental health services and support.[5] In particular, they are under-represented as users of the enabling services and over-represented in the population of patients who are admitted to, compulsorily detained in, and treated by mental health services.[6] Studies have demonstrated the experience and expectation of racist mis-treatment by mental health services alongside disproportionate admission and detention that discourages early access.[7] Under-utilisation of services has also been identified as an important factor in poor outcomes in African and Caribbean communities.[8] Further, specialist mental health services use frameworks and operate on assumptions to design services that are unsuitable or inaccessible to minority ethnic community members.[9] Concern about the welfare of African and Caribbean mental health service users has been heightened by the national census of inpatients in mental health services,[10,11] highlighting increased rates of admission and compulsory detention, and inquiries into the deaths of African and Caribbean men with mental health problems in mental health services, most recently the report into the death of David 'Rocky' Bennett.[12]

The need for mental health advocacy with African and Caribbean men is therefore clear. Advocacy may help to ensure all individuals are treated and supported under the least restrictive alternative, safeguarding their rights and enabling them to exercise choice. Advocacy has the potential to challenge inequality and discrimination as well as secure access to appropriate treatment and support. It can also serve to influence the development and design of culturally acceptable and appropriate services and increase the awareness and understanding of African and Caribbean communities of mental health issues.

However, reports of advocacy within mental health services have pointed to inequalities in access and questioned conventional models of advocacy for minority ethnic groups.[13,14] This study therefore builds on the need to define mental health advocacy, within a context of the experience of African and Caribbean men, to identify the current evidence base for the development of mental health advocacy for African and Caribbean men.

1.2 Terms of reference for the review

The review focused on the mental health advocacy needs of African and Caribbean men. The focus was on men because of their particular and well-documented vulnerability within the mental health system. Advocacy services related to legal representation at mental health tribunals, refugees or asylum seekers, and dementia are excluded, as it was considered that these forms of advocacy were for specific client need[15] and context.

1.3 Objectives for the knowledge review

The primary aim of this Knowledge Review was to establish the organisational models and principles that would support best practice in advocacy for African and Caribbean men using mental health services. The objectives were:

- to identify good practice and service development in the provision of advocacy with African and Caribbean men;
- to review the research evidence for improvements in treatment, in particular diversion to less restrictive treatment or care settings, and other outcomes that result from advocacy with African and Caribbean men;
- to identify the organisational arrangements for current practice, and the present challenges and opportunities for delivering the highest quality advocacy with African and Caribbean men;

- to explore the experiences of African and Caribbean men using specialist mental health services and their definitions of best practice in the provision of advocacy to meet their needs;
- to explore the experiences of African and Caribbean men who are users of advocacy services and non-users of advocacy to identify their views of these services, the extent to which they are meeting their needs and to identify potential areas for development;
- to explore the views of commissioners, providers of advocacy services and staff in mental health services to identify organisational arrangements and proposals for developing the capacity and sustainability of advocacy with African and Caribbean men.

1.4   Involvement of stakeholders

This work was undertaken by a partnership between the Centre for Ethnicity and Health and the Department of Nursing at the University of Central Lancashire (UCLAN), the African and Caribbean Mental Health Service, Manchester (ACMHS-Manchester), Equalities – the National Council for Disabled People and Carers from Black and Minority Ethnic Communities, London, and Lancashire Advocacy, Preston. Equalities and Lancashire Advocacy are user-led organisations with Equalities having specific expertise and established networks in relation to African and Caribbean communities and Lancashire Advocacy also having expertise with the development of advocacy. ACMHS-Manchester provides a range of mental health services to African and Caribbean communities in Manchester and also has expertise with advocacy and an extensive knowledge of service provision. These partners represent the major stakeholders in this review and have been extensively involved in shaping the project as members of the project team. Further detail on this is provided in Section 2.10 and organisational details provided in Appendix 1.

2

Methodology

This section outlines the background to the review and the method for undertaking it. It is supported by Appendix 2, which provides an overview of the policy context for the review and Appendix 3, which provides an overview of the results from the different stages. Detail on the technical aspects of the review including the search strategy, data filtration and extraction forms are available on the SCIE website at www. scie.org.uk/publications/knowledgereviews/kr15-appendices.pdf.

2.1 Background and review question

2.1.1 Ethnic differences and inequalities in mental health provision

The greater part of the currently available research reports that African and Caribbean men are over-represented in the population of patients who are compulsorily detained and treated by mental health services in comparison to the White British population. From a systematic review of pathways into and use of specialist mental health services in the UK, Bhui et al[16] concluded that Black people were four times as likely to experience compulsory detention. Most recently this has been confirmed by the annual census undertaken jointly by the Healthcare Commission and Mental Health Act Commission. In 2005,[17] this showed that admission rates were three or more times higher for Black Caribbean, Black African, Other Black and White/Black Mixed groups. Further, the rate of detention for men from these groups was 25% to 38% above average. The 2006[18] census confirmed this picture of higher rates of admission and detention, lower rates of referral from GPs and community mental health teams and higher rates of referral from the criminal justice system. The pathways into care for African and Caribbean men are therefore more problematic with low levels of general practitioner involvement and an excess of police involvement compared with the White British population.[19-21] African and Caribbean men are also over-represented in secure settings;[22] receive higher doses of medication; are more likely to be subject to control and restraint;[23] and are less likely to be referred for psychological therapies.

A number of explanations have been put forward for this pattern. Early on British psychiatrists accounted for these differences in terms of misdiagnosis reflecting unfamiliarity with beliefs of African and Caribbean communities.[24] The contribution of environmental factors, particularly social disadvantage, including racism, has also been noted.[25] More recently, it has been proposed that some of the excess in rates of compulsory detention for African and Caribbean people may be due to delays in seeking help early in their illness.[26] This may reflect dissatisfaction with service provision and there is evidence that second and third-generation African and Caribbean service users are less satisfied with services than older Caribbean-born or White service users.[27]

Two qualitative studies provide insights into the views of African and Caribbean people and their interaction with mental health services. From a series of focus groups with African and Caribbean service users, their families and carers and mental health professionals, the Sainsbury Centre for Mental Health (SCMH)[28] adopted the term 'circles of fear' to describe the different layers of fear inextricably linked with both racism and mental illness – fear of black people, fear of mental illness and fear of talking about race and culture – 'creating a pernicious cycle of fear; a circle that impacts negatively on the engagement of Black people with services and vice versa'. The combination of these fears interacts negatively to shape the interactions between Black people and mental health services. The second study by McClean et al[29] found that social exclusion emerged as a fundamental starting point for the majority of participants who asserted the experience of racist exclusion faced by Black people. Three forms of exclusion were identified: cultural, institutional and socioeconomic, which defined African and Caribbean members' interactions with mental health services. The costs of this inequality and over-representation have recently been analysed and it is estimated that in London, the total cost of mental health services for an average Black service user is 58% higher than for an average White user.[30] The picture is therefore one of inefficient, ineffective and unacceptable mental health service provision for African and Caribbean men experiencing mental health problems.

Advocacy has the potential to address this and to tackle these different forms of exclusion highlighted by the two studies above. This is confirmed by present community engagement projects designed to establish the mental health needs of African and Caribbean communities.[31] The SCMH study[32] recommends access to advocacy early on in the cycle of care and recommends that it is commissioned and provided as part of the key role of gateway agencies, whose main function is to develop bridge-building programmes to support the reintegration of Black users.

2.1.2 Policy context

Over the past decade there has been a raft of policy and other reports aimed at addressing the issues above and the acknowledged failure of mental health services to meet the needs of people from BME communities appropriately or adequately (see Appendix 2). In England, the *National Service Framework for mental health* (NSF)[33] highlighted the needs of people from BME communities and emphasised the need for the cultural sensitivity of services. This was followed by *Inside Outside*,[34] providing guidance to improve mental health services for BME communities in England.

The inquiry[35] into the death of David (Rocky) Bennett* placed the failures in his care in the context of the definiton of institutional racism in the Stephen Lawrence Report,[36] and supported the development of a BME mental health strategy. This strategy, *Delivering race equality in mental health care*,[37] built on *Inside Outside* and subsequent consultation with stakeholders, to identify three building blocks fundamental to the successful delivery of improved outcomes and experiences for people with mental health problems from BME communities. These are: better quality and more intelligent use of information, more appropriate and responsive services and increased community engagement. It also identified 12 characteristics of services that ought to be in place by 2010 for people from BME communities in contact with mental health services, and proposed the introduction of 500 community development workers (CDWs) to facilitate the realisation of these objectives.[38] They focus on improving the acceptability of mental health services and of diverting

---

* David Bennett was a 38-year-old African and Caribbean patient who died on 30 October 1998 in a medium secure psychiatric unit after being restrained by staff.

people from compulsory detention and restrictive forms of care through community engagement and workforce development. In addition the strategy recommends that primary care trusts (PCTs) and service providers ensure adequate investment in and provision of culturally appropriate independent advocacy.

Improving equality of access, treatment and outcomes for BME groups is also the focus of the Welsh Assembly's *Raising the standard: Race equality action plan for adult mental health services in Wales*.[39] Alongside this, *The revised adult mental health National Service Framework and an action plan for Wales*[40] establishes a standard for service user and carer empowerment. This action plan reports the intention to produce implementation guidance on statutory advocacy and non-statutory in-patient and community advocacy services and establishes a target for local authorities and local health boards to ensure the availability of statutory advocacy across Wales by March 2007. Similarly the Bamford mental health review in Northern Ireland[41] proposes a statutory right to independent advocacy for people experiencing mental health problems or a learning difficulty. It also recommends the development and funding of a strategy for independent advocacy to be coordinated by the Department of Health, Social Services and Public Safety.

The development of advocacy with African and Caribbean men needs to be placed in the context of current legislative and policy developments. The draft Mental Health Bill (2004)[42] proposed the right to an independent specialist mental health advocate for people detained under the Act. The subsequent amending Bill,[42a] initially made no reference to advocacy but during its passage through the Commons, amendments were made [*] to set up statutory advocacy services and placed a duty on the Secretary of State and Welsh Ministers to make arrangements to ensure that independent mental health advocates are available to certain patients detained under the 1983 Mental Health Act. The Mental Capacity Act 2005[43] covers decision making for those people whose capacity is impaired. It requires an independent mental capacity advocate (IMCA) to be appointed to aid decision making for those who are 'unbefriended' – that is, those without relatives – in other words, non-instructed ad-

---

[*] June 20th 2007

vocacy.[*] All local authorities will be required to commission an IMCA service. Together these developments have encouraged the growth of an independent professional casework model of advocacy.

Current policy developments set out proposals to increase the choice and control that people have over how their needs are met. The White Paper *Our health, our care, our say*[44] outlines a range of measures for people to take control and responsibility for their own lives, through, for example, individual budgets and Direct Payments. However, the omission of advocacy from the White Paper is seen as a serious one. In its consultation document[45] The Disability Rights Commission raises concerns about how community services will meet the expectations of the White Paper without addressing the issue of patchy provision of independent advocacy services. They argue that unless there is adequate access to independent advocacy services many people will be excluded from these initiatives.

2.1.3 The concept of advocacy

Advocacy is typically defined in terms of giving vulnerable people a voice.[46] It is grounded in an understanding of unequal power relationships between providers of health or social care services and those that receive them and is concerned with seeing the world from the service user's perspective.[47] As Silvera and Kapasi[48] make clear in their review of health advocacy for BME Londoners:

> Vulnerable people can be intimidated by the bureaucracy of statutory services, feeling powerless and voiceless ... advocacy is essential in making sure the voices of disadvantaged people are heard so that everyone can access the services and support they are entitled to.

The concept of advocacy has been criticised for being ill-defined and vague and its theoretical basis is often implied.[49] Atkinson,[50] in her literature review, identifies four components to advocacy:

---

[*] Non-instructed advocacy refers to representation of wishes on behalf of a person unable to express them, usually because of lack of capacity.

- empowerment: enabling people to be their own advocates;
- autonomy and self-determination: enabling people to be in control of their own lives;
- citizenship: safeguarding rights;
- inclusion of otherwise marginalised people.

To some extent, these themes are reflected in the current definiton, widely used by advocacy services,[51] developed by Action 4 Advocacy in their Charter[52] This states:

> Advocacy is taking action to help people say what they want, secure their rights, represent their interests and obtain the services they need. Advocates and advocacy schemes work in partnership with the people they support and take their side. Advocacy promotes social inclusion, equality and social justice.

The World Health Organisation (WHO) has identified advocacy as one of 11 areas for action in any mental health policy,[53] and points to the benefits of advocacy. These include reducing the duration of in-patient treatment, and the number of visits to health services, building self-esteem and feelings of well-being, enhancing coping skills, strengthening social networks, improving family relationships, furthering the development of implementation of programmes on mental health promotion, treatment and rehabilitation, implementing mental health legislation and improving public awareness of mental health issues.[54] For WHO, the concept of advocacy includes elements that are intended to support an individual's voice being heard and include awareness raising, information, education, training, mutual help, counselling, mediating, defending and denouncing.[55]

In the UK context, as was seen earlier, mental health advocacy has become increasingly focused and associated with protecting rights in relation to mental health legislation. This review started with a concept of advocacy as independent advocacy provided by trained staff, often described as 'professional advocacy'. However, the initial scoping review and input from the partner organisations strongly indicated that this conception did not sit easily with advocacy development for African and Caribbean communities. This echoed the study by Rai-Atkins et al,[56] who criticised the definition of independent advocacy as an individually focused endeavour that reflected western values.

Rai-Atkins et al[57] proposed the following as a culturally appropriate definition:

> Advocacy is a process rooted in the foundation of individual empowerment. It recognises that interdependence is a key attribute in achieving a sense of personhood and alliance. Advocacy therefore aims to secure 'diverse solutions for diverse needs' by applying the tenets of self-definition, equality and assistance for all people in their time of need, in ways that they choose.

This definition draws out the concept not only of individual empowerment but also of interdependence, framing advocacy as a strategy for equality and social justice. Rai-Atkins et al[58] go on to introduce the term 'community advocacy'. They describe this as follows:

> Community advocacy will strengthen the development of skills and knowledge within the community, so that people can begin to feel more valued and respected. Moreover, a community development approach can create culturally appropriate structures that will enable communities to identify and assume control of the process by becoming involved in the development of new services.

Carlisle[59] reviewed the concept of advocacy in the context of health promotion as a strategy for addressing inequalities. She developed a framework in order to locate advocacy practice, arguing that the nature of advocacy work would be influenced by the conception of health inequalities. Carlisle distinguished two dimensions – goals (empowerment vs protection/prevention) and domain or level (causes vs cases). Although a comprehensive examination of the theoretical basis for advocacy was outwith the scope of the current review, the framework developed by Carlisle has been adapted in the light of the Rai-Atkins' definition to provide a framework for analysis of the service descriptions later. This is described in Section 3.

Not only is the conception of advocacy in doubt but relatively little is known about how it should be provided to BME communities, although it has been argued that people from these communities are in greater need because their needs and wishes are at greater risk of being dismissed.[60] A systematic mapping exercise of mental health advocacy undertaken by Rai-Atkins et al[61] found relatively few Black advocacy projects in existence; that advocacy needs of BME communities were not being met by mainstream advocacy services but were, to some extent being met by community organisations, which received little if any funding for this purpose. This review therefore aims to consider how mental health advocacy should be organised for African and Caribbean men in order that they are able to have greater voice in and thus choice of the services they receive so that services provided are more appropriate and acceptable.

2.1.4 Review question

What are the optimum models of practice for mental health advocacy with African and Caribbean men?

Sub-questions:

1. What models of advocacy exist for BME communities in general, and African and Caribbean men in particular, and what factors influence their effectiveness, acceptability and accessibility?
2. What are the experiences and preferred outcomes of advocacy for BME communities in general, and African and Caribbean men in particular?
3. What is the evidence for the effectiveness of advocacy in meeting the specific needs and preferences of this client group, and of diversion to less restrictive care?

2.2 Searching

The search was undertaken in two phases. An initial scoping study was undertaken for systematic reviews, experimental evaluations of generic advocacy and policy documents relevant to mental health advocacy in BME communities, by searching the main regulatory, statutory and policy sources and systematic review databases for health and social care, using broad keyword terms for mental health, advocacy and minority ethnic communities. The policy documents and key reports identified are summarised in Appendix 2. The material identified was used to develop an initial thematic analysis and contributed to the narrative review of the contextual literature for the main review.

The strategy for the main search sought to be as inclusive as possible in order to build up knowledge in this area. The following sources were used to trace relevant material:

a) Bibliographic sources: that is, main health and social care databases for both published and unpublished research and related literature.
b) Web-based sources: including general and mental health sources, client group and advocacy-specific websites and generic internet gateways.
c) A mailshot to advocacy projects and Black mental health projects and inquiries to national organisations and institutions providing advocacy training.
d) Sources identified from the Practice Survey, user-identified sources, national and international bodies, discussion groups identified in the scoping search and from other sources and all reference to past or present projects identified by the initial internet search were followed up by direct web searching of sites.
e) Author tracing, and forward and lateral citation searching for all published research.
f) Hand searching of journals that typically do not appear in electronic databases.

The full search strategy is available at www.scie.org.uk/publications/knowledgereviews/kr15-appendices.pdf.

The initial search terms covered the major concepts of mental health, advocacy and ethnicity. Because of the potential lack of research-based literature specific to the African and Caribbean population, searches were conducted at two levels of detail: (a) all forms of evidence specifically relevant to mental health advocacy with African and Caribbean service users, and (b) research relating to the implementation and evaluation of mental health advocacy for BME communities. This is so that, in the absence of direct evidence for the target client group, principles that are adequately supported by research in the wider BME community could be identified and considered for transferability. The search process has been highly iterative given that much of the relevant material has been grey literature.

2.3 Criteria for inclusion of studies in the review

2.3.1 Type of client

The review primarily considered evidence relating to adult (that is, over the age of 16) male service users or their carers/families, of African and Caribbean descent. Evidence relating to mental health advocacy services for Black British communities in general was also considered, if it was likely that African and Caribbean individuals would have been included but not differentiated. The definition of mental health included all forms of mental illness, or the promotion of mental health. Clients with learning disabilities or substance misuse were excluded, unless they had a dual diagnosis incorporating mental illness.

2.3.2 Type of intervention

Advocacy services in the context of mental health were included, from any service type, for example, forensic, criminal justice, community, primary care, and from any service provider, for example, lay, community, voluntary, statutory.

2.3.3 Types of outcome

Evidence was sought relating to outcomes for both the service user and their carer/family, and the service, including:

a) Client/carer outcomes, for example, involvement, empowerment, integration, engagement, as measured by client self-report.
b) Service use, for example, admission, exclusion, detention, diversion.
c) Client/carer views on services, for example, satisfaction, acceptability, accessibility.
d) Service and economic outcomes, for example, referral rates, cost of service.

2.3.4 Types of evidence

The review included all descriptive, evaluative or empirical material reporting the provision of, need for, or experience of advocacy services for African and Caribbean men. Evidence was limited to literature published in English from 1994, when the NHS Executive instructed all service providers to collect data on service users' ethnic origins, to 31 July 2006.

2.3.5 Inclusion criteria

- *Client group:* Black Caribbean, Black African, African-Caribbean, Mixed African/White, Mixed Caribbean/White, Black British; Male; Adult (16 plus).
- *Definition of mental health:* general descriptions, for example, mental illness and specific diagnoses, schizophrenia and depression. Including learning disabilities and substance misuse with mental illness.
- *Contexts of advocacy services:* primary care, voluntary sector, mental health services, forensic and secure services and the criminal justice system.
- *Stakeholder outcomes:* the range of service user and service outcomes were considered are acceptability, accessibility, satisfaction, appropriateness, integration, engagement, being informed, empowerment, diversion from acute in-patient care or the criminal justice system etc.
- *Service outcomes:* factors influencing implementation, service changes and developments, resourcing.
- *Literature:* the search was limited to literature published from 1994 to 31 July 2006. It was limited to material published in English due to the limitations of resources and the timescale.

2.3.6 Exclusion criteria

- Papers published in languages other than English
- Papers published on or before 31 December 1993
- Papers relating to children aged 16 or under

- Papers concerned generally with mental illness in the African and Caribbean community that did not relate to advocacy
- Papers concerned solely with refugees and asylum seekers
- Papers concerned solely with dementia advocacy
- Papers concerned solely with learning disabilities or substance misuse, not in combination with mental health problems (that is, dual diagnosis).

2.4 Keywording

From the mapping following the scoping review and subsequent thematic analysis a keywording system was developed to capture the attributes of the different sources of evidence. The framework for keywording is provided online at www.scie.org.uk/publications/knowledgereviews/ kr15-appendices.pdf.

2.5 Results

A total of 4,539 items were downloaded from bibliographic databases. A further 315 items were identified from web-based searching, personal communication, hand and citation searching, resulting in a total of 4,854 items. After removal of duplicates, 3,705 records were progressed to screening. The results of the search are summarised in Appendix 3. The evidence types included research reports, descriptive or evaluative accounts of need, experience or outcome produced by advocacy projects (including material contained in projects' annual reports), conference proceedings, course materials, and accounts produced by individual service users, community organisations and advocacy providers.

2.6 In-depth review

A total of 148 papers were identified that fit the inclusion criteria and were classified into two groups on the basis of their relevance to the review question: primary (that is, directly relevant) and secondary (that is, indirectly relevant). The secondary material is presented first as it provided a basis for developing the conceptual framework for the analysis of the primary material. Table 1 in Section 3 provides an overview.

2.6.1 Secondary material

Research, service descriptions or practice guidelines that are:

a) indirectly relevant to the client group (for example, evaluation of advocacy and standards/guidelines for advocacy for a wider ethnic group) or

b) indirectly relevant to advocacy (for example, description of user experiences of a mental health service specifically for African and Caribbean men).

Data was extracted from 97 papers in tabular form to capture the needs of African and Caribbean men, how advocacy might work for BME communities and African and Caribbean men and potential outcomes using a thematic content analysis, and a summary of this is presented online at www.scie.org.uk/publications/knowledgereviews/kr15-appendices.pdf. Findings concerning the characteristics of advocacy provision were also extracted and this was used to develop a typology, available at Appendix 5.

Evidence contained in standards and guidelines was extracted in tabular form to identify the principles and recommendations for the provision of advocacy for BME communities in general and African and Caribbean men, in particular, and the analysis is provided online at www.scie.org.uk/publications/knowledgereviews/kr15-appendices.pdf.

2.6.2 Primary material

Fifty-one papers were identified that were directly relevant to client group, context and service outcomes and this material comprises the main body of literature to be synthesised.

Three different types of material were identified; descriptive and evaluative studies; service descriptions; and relevant commentary. An in-depth analysis was undertaken on the first two types of evidence, with 10 papers relating to 9 studies and 36 service descriptions that were not evaluative. A significant amount of commentary in fact referred to these sources and although while interesting, was judged not to add significantly to it. The relevant data extraction forms for each of the different types of evidence and the results of the analyses are provided online at www.scie.org.uk/publications/knowledgereviews/kr15-appendices.pdf.

Evidence contained in the descriptive and evaluative studies was extracted in terms of (a) the intervention described in the study, (b) its impact as defined in terms of the outcomes specified in the review protocol, (c) its implementation, and (d) service users' experiences.

Evidence contained in the project descriptions was extracted as fully as was possible in terms of their characteristics – definition of advocacy, focus, paid/unpaid, individual/group, proactive/reactive, trained/untrained, independent/related to services/short-term /long-term and relationship to the community.

2.7. Quality appraisal

The evidence was evaluated using a quality appraisal tool based on the TAPUPAS standards described by Pawson et al[62] and evaluated by Long et al,[63] which considers:

- Transparency (Is it open to scrutiny?)
- Accuracy (Are the findings and conclusions credible?)
- Purposivity (Is it fit for purpose?)
- Utility (Is it fit for use by others?)
- Propriety (Is it legal and ethical?)
- Accessibility (Is it well presented and accessible?)
- Specificity (Does it meet standards for the type of knowledge?).[64]

This framework of questions was used, as appropriate, for the different types of evidence for the in-depth review. Two reviewers applied the quality criteria independently. An adapted version of the AGREE instrument[65] was used to evaluate the standards and good practice guidelines. In addition the strength of evidence was considered and in particular its relevance to the review question. Time constraints limited the involvement of the partner organisations in this process. No material was excluded from the review on the basis of quality, but quality issues influencing interpretation are presented.

2.8　Analysis of the findings

2.8.1　Conceptual review of secondary material

The secondary material consisted of research, service descriptions or practice guidelines that were indirectly relevant to mental health advocacy provision for African and Caribbean men, but directly relevant to the provision of mental health advocacy for the BME community, or to the needs of African and Caribbean men in a mental health context. A thematic narrative analysis of this material was undertaken to map the needs and problems of the client group, the characteristics of advocacy provision, the potential mechanisms of action by which advocacy might impact on outcomes, the range of desirable and undesirable outcomes and the barriers and facilitators to the development and provision of advocacy services that have been identified from the empirical and conceptual literature (online at www.scie.org.uk/publications/knowledgereviews/kr15-appendices.pdf). From this mapping exercise, a preliminary typology of models of mental health advocacy was developed (see Appendix 5), and a conceptual model for use as a framework for the analysis of the findings from the primary material was constructed. The analysis of this material is presented in Section 3 of this report.

2.8.2　Analysis of primary material

The primary material consisted of description, research or evaluation that was directly relevant to the provision of mental health advocacy with African and Caribbean men. Each type of material was grouped and thematically analysed in terms of the evidence it provided for (a) the needs of the client group, (b) the process and implementation of advocacy, (c) the outcomes of advocacy, and (d) the barriers and facilitators to the development of model advocacy services.

The analysis of this material is presented in Section 4. Findings from the Research review have been drawn together in Section 5 to provide a description and evaluation of the strength of evidence from the review for:

- current models of mental health advocacy provision for African and Caribbean men;

- features of best practice and factors influencing the provision of best practice in relation to the specific needs of the client group;
- the (actual and potential) impact of different types of advocacy provision on individual and organisational outcomes.

2.9 Synthesis of the data

In the final stage, the evidence from the in-depth review and the Practice Survey were combined to provide a description of the current provision of advocacy, and to compare and categorise the provision in terms of the models of advocacy defined by the literature.

A conceptual framework was developed for the synthesis from the analysis of the secondary literature and the views of service users, expressed either during focus groups or interviews. The analysis of the secondary literature is available online at www.scie.org.uk/publications/knowledgereviews/kr15-appendices.pdf and the views of service users, mapped using Banxia Decision Explorer* from direct quotes, are provided online at www.scie.org.uk/publications/knowledgereviews/kr15-appendices.pdf.

The conceptual framework for synthesising the material reflected the review aims and the key headings are:

- Needs and experiences of African and Caribbean men
- Outcomes identified for advocacy
- Characteristics of advocates and services for African and Caribbean men
- Organisational arrangements for advocacy
- Barriers and facilitators to the development of advocacy with African and Caribbean men.

The evidence from both the Research Review and the Practice Survey was summarised, mapped and evaluated against these headings and this analysis is provided online at www.scie.org.uk/publications/knowledgereviews/kr15-appendices.pdf.

---

* www.banxia.com

2.10 Stakeholder involvement in the review

The partnership between the university and African and Caribbean, service user and advocacy organisations was key to facilitating involvement of different stakeholders in the review. These partners were members of the project team and the Project Steering Group. Between them the representation included service users, an African and Caribbean mental health service provider and advocacy providers. This partnership approach and the experience and networks of the partner organisations no doubt facilitated engagement with African and Caribbean men with mental health problems, who are not well represented in other studies of advocacy.[66] It also ensured the relevance and accountability of the review to stakeholders.

The project team met on a regular basis to shape the direction of the review; develop the methodology; share experience of collecting data; discuss the emergent findings; comment on drafts of the report and agree a strategy for dissemination the findings. In terms of the Research review the partners, and to a lesser extent the Project Steering Group, were directly involved in:

- defining the scope and parameters of the review
- identifying literature
- identifying relevant outcomes
- commenting on the findings from the review.

The partners were more extensively involved in the Practice survey and detail on this is provided in Section 7. The method for synthesising the findings from the Research Review and the Practice Survey also directly drew on the views expressed by African and Caribbean men during the focus groups and interviews.

Overview of the literature

3.1 Introduction

This section provides an overview of the literature identified and the thematic analysis of the secondary material, which both provides a context and a framework for the analysis of the primary material. It covers the needs of African and Caribbean men experiencing mental health problems; how mental health advocacy could enable these to be addressed; factors influencing its implementation; standards and good practice; and training materials for the provision of advocacy.

3.2 Summary of the material identified

A total of 148 papers were included in the Research review. These were classified into two groups: 51 met the criteria for inclusion as primary papers and 97 for inclusion as secondary papers. An overview of the different types of papers for each group is provided in Table 1. In addition 47 papers were identified that it was not possible to retrieve. This was either because they were initial reports of current research not yet completed (18) or organisational change, particularly in the NHS, making it difficult to track the original paper. Of these 47, it was judged that 12 were relevant and were likely to fit the criteria for inclusion (2 as primary papers and 10 as secondary papers).

A thematic analysis of the secondary material was undertaken in terms of needs, models, mechanisms of action, outcomes and barriers and facilitators to implementation. This is presented in tabular form online at www.scie.org.uk/publications/knowledgereviews/kr15-appendices.pdf, with details of the papers and type of evidence. It provides a platform for the analysis of the primary literature.

3.3 Mental health needs of African and Caribbean men experiencing mental distress

There are a number of recent reviews and key studies that have identified inequalities in the treatment and experience of African and Caribbean men in relation to mental health services. They point to:

- A negative relationship between mental health services and African and Caribbean men resulting in a lack of inclination to seek help or comply with treatment, leading to relapse and readmission. This reflects a lack of understanding of cultural norms and beliefs, a denial or ignorance of the experience of racism and exclusion faced by African and Caribbean men and a conception of mental health that reflects western values. Associated with this can be stereotyping and racism resulting in a fundamental mistrust and suspicion of services. The consequences of these difficulties are poor engagement with mainstream service and dissatisfaction.
- Less desirable and effective pathways into care with a higher rate of compulsory admission, low level of general practitioner (GP) involvement and an excess of police involvement compared with the White population.
- Restrictions on choice with African and Caribbean men being less likely to be offered psychological treatments and more likely to receive physical treatment at a more intensive level. These restrictions are interpreted as indicative of racism and contributing to the 'circles of fear'.[67]
- Social exclusion and disadvantage, with perceptions of discriminatory treatment deterring African and Caribbean people from accessing mental health services and broader disadvantage in terms of education and employment.

Table 1
Papers meeting criteria for inclusion

Type of evidence	Classification	Number	Country of origin
Policy	Primary	0	–
	Secondary	12	7 England, 1 Wales, 1 Northern Ireland, 1 Scotland, 2 international
Standards or good practice guidelines	Primary	3 included in systematic inquiry	England
	Secondary	11	9 England, 2 Scotland
Training course descriptions	Primary	0	–
	Secondary	3	England
Service or project descriptions	Primary	36: 4 papers refer to 2 projects and 1 paper refers to over 20 projects, although not entirely clear how many provide advocacy	32 England, 3 Wales, 1 Northern Ireland
	Secondary	2	England

Table 1 continued

Type of evidence	Classification	Number	Country of origin
Systematic inquiry	Primary	10 referring to 9 studies	8 studies in England, 1 in Scotland
	Secondary	38, the majority focused on needs or epidemiological differences	1 European, 1 USA, 1 Caribbean, remainder UK/England
Conference proceedings	Primary	0	–
	Secondary	1, collection of papers	England
Commentary including service user and practitioner commentary	Primary	5 predominantly referring to the studies above	England
	Secondary	30 highlighting findings from key reports and/or calling for action to be taken. Includes a small number of theoretical papers	1 USA, remainder UK/England

3.4 How mental health advocacy could empower African and Caribbean men

3.4.1 The need for advocacy

Advocacy is identified as a way of addressing the issues above and ensuring that African and Caribbean men access appropriate and less damaging services. There have now been a number of reports and groups that have identified an urgent need for Black mental health advocacy.[68] *Delivering race equality* identified the development of mental health advocacy for BME communities as a key area of activity for PCTs. *Breaking the circles of fear* also called for good quality advocacy to be offered as early a possible, before problems arose, so that early access, and early interventions within less threatening and damaging settings could be facilitated. This is echoed by The Civis Trust in their study of early intervention for Asian and African and Caribbean communities[69] and more widely by a significant amount of commentary.

3.4.2 Defining advocacy

It was evident from the main search that the term 'advocacy' is imprecisely defined. We found that advocacy was used to describe support groups, whose aim may have been to improve knowledge and information about available services but were not designed as a mechanism for negotiation or representation.[70] Conversely, it was used to describe the role of a key worker in mental health services, sometimes described as a case advocate.[71] More generally, the lack of precision in defining advocacy echoes Heer's[72] observation that there is general agreement about the fundamental principles of advocacy but significant disagreement over where its boundaries lie.

Definitions and distinguishing characteristics of different types of advocacy were identified from the secondary material, as described in Appendix 5. The types of advocacy identified are:

- *Citizen:* a person from the community supports an individual and represents their wishes.
- *Self:* the individual expresses and represents their own views.

- *Peer:* someone with experience of using mental health services supports and speaks on behalf of someone else.
- *Community:* a community represents their views in order to protect and enhance the status of community members.
- *Collective or group:* people with similar experiences represent their shared views on behalf of the group. User groups and patient councils are an example.
- *Professional (also referred to as specialist or instructed):* trained and paid advocates who provide a service to protect an individual's rights through information, assistance and representation.
- *Legal:* representation of an individual's wishes and interests during a legal process.
- *Non-instructed:* representation of wishes on behalf of a person unable to express them, usually because of lack of capacity.

Clearly any individual organisation might be providing some or all of these types of advocacy. The distinguishing characteristics that were identified, relevant to the organisation of advocacy, are:

- focus: individual or group
- proactive/reactive
- short term/long term
- independence/interdependence with service provision
- paid/unpaid
- trained/untrained
- similar/different identity from advocacy partners (gender, shared heritage, experience of mental health issues, service user, sexual orientation, disability etc)
- community participation: organic/designed/none.

3.4.3 Advocacy and African and Caribbean men

Figure 1 provides a framework for locating mental health advocacy for African and Caribbean men, adapted from the framework by Carlisle[73] and using the dimensions of independence and interdependence to reflect Rai-Atkins et al's[74] definition of culturally appropriate advocacy. This draws out the differences between types of advocacy and their

Figure 1
Conceptual framework

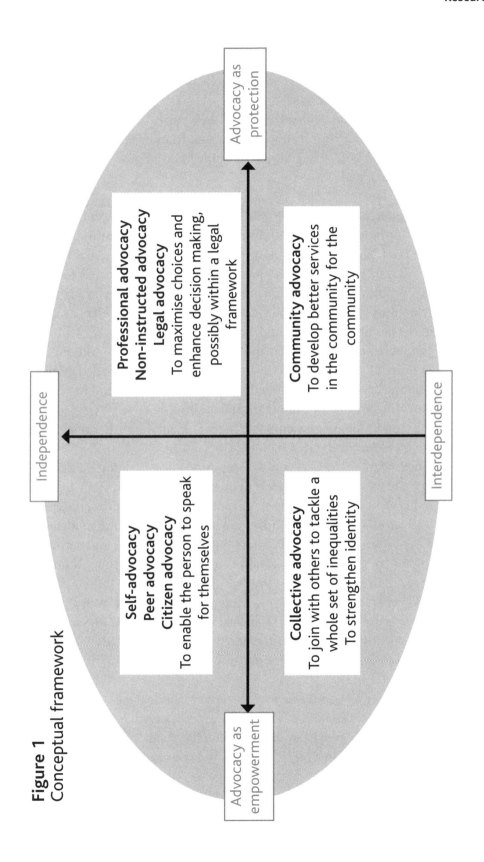

focus. Advocacy for African and Caribbean men could be located in any or all of the quadrants.

The major themes identified as to how advocacy could work for African and Caribbean men were identified from conceptual mapping (online at www.scie.org.uk/publications/knowledgereviews/kr15-appendices.pdf), and are:

- *Improving the quality of mental health service experience* so that services are more responsive and understand social and cultural issues by developing meaningful communication between African and Caribbean men and service providers, challenging constructions of the 'problem', shifting the emphasis on to underlying needs from symptoms or diagnosis and through the involvement of service users in the design and provision of services.
- *Increasing control and choices* and in particular identifying alternatives to hospital admission, increasing access to psychological therapies, securing choices in relation to living and employment and in general providing information about mental health issues and services so that the men become knowledgeable users of mental health services and are more involved in decision making.
- *Supporting and strengthening identity* by positively valuing Black identity and focusing on unlocking potential and promoting citizenship rather than dependency on services. BME mental health services are likely to emphasise inequalities, power relations and cultural identity. They typically build on the stress-buffering, advocacy and befriending role of existing organisations such as a church group, informal networks and community groups.
- *Addressing social disadvantage and social exclusion* at all levels through tackling underlying social problems, addressing inequalities in provision, identifying and securing acceptable accommodation, opening up routes into employment and providing access to welfare rights information.
- *Stimulating the development of alternative models of mental health care from a Black perspective.* The evidence indicates that locating Black mental health provision in the voluntary sector creates the opportunity for more flexible, responsive and culturally sensitive services, for example Afro-centric counselling. Such services reflect the needs of the community by truly having 'organic roots' in the community

and staffing by Black workers provides a positive experience of inclusion.

- *Protecting and promoting human rights.* This is a fundamental goal of advocacy. It can provide representation on specific issues and in relation to African and Caribbean men advocacy has the potential to tackle discrimination and the deleterious effects of racism.
- *Raising awareness of mental health issues in the community* in order to reduce stigma and facilitate early access to appropriate support.

3.5 Outcomes from advocacy

From the conceptual mapping of key reports and views of the project team, six key areas of outcomes, that advocacy could have a positive impact on, were also identified:

- Changes in its service provision so that service users receive a more culturally appropriate and effective service.
- Changes in treatment so that service users receive a greater range of treatments more quickly delivered more consistently and to a higher standard of care.
- Changes in the relationship between services and the individual so that there is earlier access to appropriate care and greater choice; diversion from more restrictive forms of care and early attention to and resolution of problems resulting in better engagement, better management of mental health issues, less use of in-patient mental health services and greater satisfaction with service provision.
- Changes in the family and/or support system by increasing the acceptance and awareness of mental health issues and activating more community support.
- Changes in the person reflected as increased confidence and ability to get on with life and with other people.
- Changes in the civil status of the individual so that they are more able to fully participate in civic and social roles.

Evidence for the impact of advocacy in terms of these outcome areas was searched for as part of the in-depth review.

3.6. Factors influencing implementation of mental health advocacy

Twelve papers identified factors that are relevant to the implementation of mental health advocacy, largely from consideration of factors influencing the development of the Black voluntary and community sector (BVCS). Silvera and Kapasi,[75] from their study of health advocacy providers for BME communities in London, identified the following areas as key to the development of advocacy for BME communities:

- improving the funding and commissioning of advocacy;
- building capacity among advocacy providers;
- policy development and research;
- developing standards;
- developing and supporting easier access to standardised accredited training;
- strengthening networks and partnerships.

The capacity and sustainability of the BVCS and its unequal status vis-à-vis other voluntary sector groups were consistently identified as major barriers to its successful development. This inequality was also reflected in partnerships with other voluntary sector groups and the statutory sector and the relatively under-developed mechanisms for service user involvement in mainstream developments. Approaches that aimed to outreach and engage with communities were identified as essential in making advocacy more accessible. This commitment to accessibility needs to be grounded in an open and honest approach that acknowledges inequalities in and the limitations of mainstream approaches. Resources, both money and training for staff, along with a profile for the role of BVCS in relation to advocacy were also identified as critical for success.

Although not explicitly mentioned, the demographic profile of a particular location and distinct population needs are likely to influence the development of specific advocacy provision for African and Caribbean men. The study of the understanding and expectations of BME communities of independent advocacy by Bowes et al[76] is relevant here. They found no systematic inter-ethnic variability between different BME communities to members of the same ethnic group often showing marked differences of experience and preferences. Although the engage-ment of African and Caribbean communities in the study was weak, this study raises the question of how to ensure the most appropriate way of meeting diverse advocacy needs in a specific locality.

3.7 Standards for the organisation and provision of mental health advocacy with Black and minority ethnic communities

Fourteen publications relevant to the development of high-quality mental health advocacy services for African and Caribbean men were identified. None of these focused specifically on the provision of mental health advocacy with the African and Caribbean community. The most relevant were three publications focused on BME communities and the first two have been included in the in-depth review:

- Rai-Atkins et al's[77] recommendations for good practice in mental health advocacy for BME communities.
- Guidance, published by the Mayor of London (Chouhan and MacCattram),[78] for the development of BVCS providing mental health services, including advocacy.
- Kapasi and Silvera's[79] standards framework for delivering health advocacy for BME Londoners.

The remaining 11 publications included standards or guidelines in rela-tion to mental health advocacy (7), or generic advocacy (4). Two sets of standards have been developed by local organisations and have been included as examples of standards developed in this way. Just under a third (4) used a systematic approach to identifying other forms of evidence although several more have involved service users and relevant organisations in the development of the guidance. The implications for implementation are largely unconsidered, with one or two notable exceptions. A summary of these standards including the quality appraisal is summarised in Table 2.

Table 2
Summary of standards and guidelines for advocacy

Publication details	Format	Reference to African and Caribbean men	Quality appraisal
Mind (2006) *With us in mind: Service user recommendations for advocacy standards in England*[86]	Describes findings and provides recommendations for mental health advocacy providers, commissioners and service user advocacy agencies.	Yes	See quality appraisal in Section 4.
Action 4 Advocacy (2006) *Quality standards for advocacy schemes*[87]	Builds on a process of establishing clear principles for advocacy, ie the Advocacy Charter (2002), which also provides the basis for a code of practice for advocates.	Not specifically	Developed with input from practitioners but no systematic review of the evidence base apparent. Well presented, providing a clear description of the standards and examples of evidence that they are being met. This would provide a useful basis for audit. It provides tools for implementation with training exercises and a list of policies and documents required to meet the standards.

Table 2 continued

Publication details	Format	Reference to African and Caribbean men	Quality appraisal
Brent Advocacy Concerns (2005) *Standards manual* (draft edition)[88]	Describes Brent Advocacy Concerns' services, how it operates and a set of standards.	Not specifically	In draft form.
Leeds Advocacy Network (2005) *Leeds advocacy standards*[89]	A set of standards signed up to by NHS trusts and Leeds City Council social services department. A poster and pack describing 12 standards.	Not specifically	Highly accessible with a poster clearly describing the standards in terms of what people can expect from advocacy. Developed by a network of advocacy services across Leeds. The basis for development including the evidence base was not clear and the implications for implementation were not identified.

Table 2 continued

Publication details	Format	Reference to African and Caribbean men	Quality appraisal
Chouhan, K. and MacAttram, M. (2005) *Towards a blueprint for action: Building capacity in the Black and minority ethnic voluntary and community sector providing mental health services*[90]	Report commissioned by the African and Caribbean Mental Health Commission. Makes recommendations on the development of BVCS providing mental health services on the basis of a descriptive survey of 25 BVCS organisations with 12 providing advocacy with African and Caribbean communities, and 12 statutory bodies or funders.	Aimed at BVCS and relevant to organisations providing mental health advocacy with African and Caribbean communities.	See quality appraisal in Section 4.

Table 2 continued

Publication details	Format	Reference to African and Caribbean men	Quality appraisal
Wood, P. and UK Advocacy Network (2004) *Advocacy standards: Standards for advocacy in mental health*[91]	A set of standards targeted at advocacy providers.	None or to BME groups more widely.	Circulated to 260 UK Advocacy Network (UKAN) member groups and national organisations and incorporates feedback from these organisations. Little detail on development, implications for implementation although does consider the relationship between service user and advocate and advocate and advocacy provider.

Table 2 continued

Publication details	Format	Reference to African and Caribbean men	Quality appraisal
Advocacy 2000 (2002) *Principles and standards in independent advocacy organsiations and groups*[92]	In three parts, it describes principles and standards for the practice of an independent advocacy organisation and describes the practice of independent and collective self-advocacy groups.	Specific focus on mental health advocacy with BME communities.	These principles and standards were developed through consultation with advocacy projects, workshops and consultation with stakeholders although the extent of service user, particularly from BME communities, is unclear. This is aimed at organisations. The broad principles for practice are clear but they cover a range of advocacy for a range of unspecified client groups. The implications for implementation are therefore not well developed.

Table 2 continued

Publication details	Format	Reference to African and Caribbean men	Quality appraisal
Rai-Atkins, A. et al (2002) *Best practice in mental health: Advocacy for African, Caribbean and South Asian communities*[94]	Reports findings and lays out recommendations for good practice in mental health advocacy for African, Caribbean and South Asian communities.	Yes. Specific focus on BME advocacy but broader than mental health.	See quality appraisal in Section 4.
Kapasi, R. and Silvera, M. (2002) *A standards framework for delivering effective health and social care advocacy for Black and minority ethnic Londoners*[93]	A toolkit for advocacy providers and commissioners. Provides a set of core and aspirational standards for health and social care advocacy and a process for implementing them.	Not specifically	Provides a clear and unambiguous set of standards. The basis for their development is not entirely clear although presumably developed from the authors' previous survey of health advocacy providers to BME Londoners. The implications for implementation could have been strengthened.

Table 2 continued

Publication details	Format	Reference to African and Caribbean men	Quality appraisal
Scottish Executive (2001) *Independent advocacy: A guide for commissioners*[97]	Follows on from a good practice guide to provide guidance for commissioners to enable them to develop detailed proposals for locally based independent advocacy schemes.	None or to BME groups more widely	This predominantly outlines a process of consulting with local stakeholders, identifying options and funding independent advocacy. The evidence base is not clear, although commissioners and other stakeholders were involved in its development. It is an accessible document, outlining different options for how advocacy might be developed with considerable latitude for local interpretation.

Table 2 continued

Publication details	Format	Reference to African and Caribbean men	Quality appraisal
UK Advocacy network (1994) *Advocacy: A code of practice*[98]	A code of practice to clarify the roles and functions of groups, advocates and advocacy workers. Has a series of chapters on different types of advocacy.	None or to BME groups more widely	This is largely descriptive as there will have been little evidence to draw on at the time it was written.
Read, J. and Wallcraft, J. (1994) *Guidelines on advocacy for mental health workers*[99]	Described as guidelines but essentially provides an overview of advocacy, its history, types of advocacy, relationship between mental health workers and advocacy, and sources of further information. It provides examples of three BME projects.	Not specifically	This is well presented and provides an explanation of advocacy and draws attention to areas of difficulty in its implementation. However, the basis for the development of the guidelines is not entirely clear. It would have been strenghtened by a systematic exploration of the options.

Those standards focused on BME communities emphasise the importance of sustainable funding, involvement of BME organisations in the development of advocacy and the need to establish fair and equitable funding for BME organisations.

There are obviously clear concerns about sustainability and capacity within this sector. Choice of advocate and a minimum standard of cultural competence are emphasised, particularly in the report by Rai-Atkins et al[80] who propose that adherence to minimum standards of cultural competence should be a precondition for statutory funding.

The guidance on mental health advocacy and generic advocacy emphasises the importance of advocacy being independent, with a distinction being drawn between structural, operational and psychological independence by Advocacy 2000.[81] The guidance tends to cover accountability and management; training, policies and procedures; confidentiality; complaints; monitoring and evaluation. There is little attention to the range of diverse needs, although reference to cultural diversity is evident in all of the guidance. The majority of the standards point to the importance of equal opportunities policies, and the need to have services accessible for all, without providing the necessary detail. Both the Mind guidance[82] and that from Brent Advocacy Concerns[83] stress the importance of bilingual advocates. Barnes et al[84] highlight the importance of linking with BME services that could provide appropriate advocacy support. Indeed the need to involve BME community organisations in the development of advocacy provision is a consistent theme and Mullins and Wood,[85] for example, point to the importance of a range of mechanisms to ensure that services are appropriate to BME communities and their changing needs.

3.8 Training materials

No relevant training needs analyses were identified although an analysis of needs in relation to generic advocacy across London was identified.[100]

Course materials from two educational programmes were obtained, neither of which was taking place for the current academic year (2006-07). The course run at UCLAN was specific to mental health advocacy and was aimed at paid advocates, leading to a University Advanced Certificate in Mental Health Advocacy. The other course at the

University of East London is scheduled to run from September 2007 and provides a Higher Education Certificate in Health Advocacy. On both courses, a proportion of student learning was directed towards understanding discrimination, equality and diversity issues. In addition training is also provided for the advocacy sector by capacity building organisations, for example Action 4 Advocacy, with courses specifically on advocacy for BME communities as well as training tailored to meet specific needs.[101]

4

In-depth review

Although nearly 150 papers were identified that fitted the criteria for the review, the specificity of these papers was limited. The previous section distilled the findings from the secondary material. This section provides a summary of the in-depth review of material judged to be directly relevant to the review question. This primary material includes a limited number of evaluative studies and a much greater number of unpublished service descriptions or accounts of projects.

4.1 Evaluative studies of advocacy and African and Caribbean men

Nine evaluative studies were identified and an overview is provided in Table 3 and online at www.scie.org.uk/publications/knowledgereviews/ kr15-appendices.pdf. As can be seen there were no studies that focused solely on the provision of mental health advocacy with African and Caribbean men. The studies identified are predominantly descriptive.

The extent of service user involvement in these studies is not always clear. Of note is the study by Christie and Hill[102] – a service user-led study of visits to seven different Black mental health projects, including four African and Caribbean services. The Mind inquiry[103] also extensively involved service users, including consultation with African and Caribbean service users, to establish mental health advocacy standards and to discuss the emergent findings in depth.

The three studies that focused on African and Caribbean communities did so in the context of mental heath provision including advocacy and the findings in relation to advocacy, were consequently embedded in general findings about mental health provision to African and Caribbean communities. The other six studies that focused on mental health advocacy have done so for the wider ethnic population and it was not always possible to tease out specific findings for African and Caribbean men.

The nature of the evidence provided by the studies differs. Two of the studies (Coleman and Dunmur;[104] Platzer and Foley)[105] were primarily concerned with needs in relation to mental health advocacy and mapping existing provision – including the views of stakeholders – drawing conclusions about its organisation. Four studies, using survey methodology or visits to services, were primarily concerned in drawing out the good practice in relation to either mental health services for BME communities including African and Caribbean communities (Chouhan and MacAttram;[106] Christie and Hill),[107] mental health advocacy and BME communities (Rai-Atkins et al)[108] or the provision of mental health advocacy to diverse populations including BME communities (Mind)[109]. Two studies focused on mental health advocacy in secure settings and reported findings in relation to process (McKeown et al)[110] and impact (Barnes and Tate),[111] while the final study (Watters, 1996)[163] was an evaluation of a multiracial mental health team, with an explicit focus on African and Caribbean communities.

4.1.1 Quality appraisal

A summary of the quality appraisal and strength of the studies in relation to the review question is provided in Table 4.

The strength of the evidence is fairly weak. Only two studies directly answering the review question were identified (Rai-Atkins et al;[121] Foley and Platzer),[122] and both were of reasonable or good quality. While the remaining studies are clearly relevant, data extraction in terms of advocacy-related activity or African and Caribbean men specifically was limited. To some extent this was a difficulty for the two main studies too. Rai-Atkins et al (2002) considered the provision for mental health advocacy for different BME communities within Yorkshire and the East Midlands – African, African Caribbean and South Asian communities – and themed their findings making it difficult to identify the specific issues in relation to provision for African and Caribbean men. Similarly the study by Platzer and Foley[123] largely considered mental health advocacy provision in relation to BME communities generally.

A major shortcoming of all the studies in directly answering the review question is the absence of evaluative methodologies so that while it is relatively clear what might be preferred, the evidence in relation to mental health advocacy having an impact on the outcome areas identified earlier is weak.

Table 3
Overview of evaluative studies

Study details	Focus		Context	Type of study
Relevance to study group	*Advocacy focus*	*Population focus*		
Chouhan, K. and MacAttram, M. (2005) *Towards a blueprint for action: Building capacity in the Black and minority ethnic voluntary and community sector providing mental health services*[112]	Mental health advocacy as part of broader mental health service provision	African and Caribbean communities	BME and BVCS providing mental health services	Descriptive survey of service providers and funders
Christie, Y. & Hill, N. (2003) *Black Spaces Project*[113]	Mental health advocacy as part of broader mental health service provision	BME communities with specific focus on African and Caribbean communities	BME mental health services in England and Wales	Descriptive survey

Table 3 continued

Study details Relevance to study group	Focus		Context	Type of study
	Advocacy focus	*Population focus*		
Watters, C. (1996) 'Inequalities in mental health: the inner city mental health project', *Journal of Community & Applied Social Psychology*, vol 6, pp 383-94[114]	Mental health advocacy as part of broader mental health service provision	BME communities with specific focus on African and Caribbean communities	African and Caribbean mental health service for people with serious mental illness (smi) living in an inner-city area	Descriptive
Platzer, H. and Foley, R. (2004) *Mental health advocacy in London: A mapping report*[115]	Mental health advocacy	General with reference to BME communities	Mental health advocacy providers across London	Descriptive survey using mixed methods

Table 3 continued

Study details Relevance to study group	Focus		Context	Type of study
	Advocacy focus	Population focus		
Mind (2006) *With us in mind: Service user recommendations for advocacy standards in England*[116]	Mental health advocacy	General with specific findings reported for African and Caribbean communities	Community	Descriptive survey
Rai-Atkins, A., Jama, A.A., Wright, N., Scott, V., Perring, C., Craig, G. and Katbamna, S. (2002) *Best practice in mental health: Advocacy for African, Caribbean and South Asian communities*[117]	BME mental health advocacy	BME communities with specific findings reported for African and Caribbean communities	Mental health advocacy providers, both mainstream and BME	Descriptive survey and multiple case study
McKeown, M., Bingley, W. and Denoual, I (2002) *Review of advocacy services at the Edenfield Regional Secure Unit and Bowness High Dependency Unit, Prestwich Hospital*[118]	Mental health advocacy in secure settings	General with specific findings reported for African and Caribbean communities	Mental health advocacy providers (mainstream and BME) in a medium secure to a high dependency unit	Process evaluation

Table 3 continued

Study details	Focus		Context	Type of study
Relevance to study group	*Advocacy focus*	*Population focus*		
Coleman, C. and Dunmur, J. (2001) *Surveying mental health advocacy needs in Sheffield*[119]	Mental health advocacy	General with reference to BME communities	Mental health advocacy providers (mainstream and BME) in Sheffield	Descriptive survey
Barnes, D. and Tate, A. (2000) *Advocacy from the outside inside: A review of the patients' advocacy service at Ashworth Hospital*[120]	Independent mental health advocacy in secure settings	General with reference to BME communities	Mainstream mental health advocacy provider in a special hospital	Process and impact evaluation

4.1.2 Advocacy provision

The two mapping studies, by Rai-Atkins et al[134] in the Trent and Yorkshire NHS region and that by Platzer and Foley[135] in London, point to serious gaps in advocacy provision for BME communities. Rai-Atkins et al[136] highlight the difficulties for BME communities in accessing mainstream provision; the lack of bilingual advocates; lack of awareness of advocacy provision among BME communities; and the different understandings of advocacy. Platzer and Foley,[137] on the other hand, found the location of advocacy groups for BME communities across London was not matched to demand, as suggested by demographic data.

Both the studies of mental health advocacy within a secure setting (McKeown et al;[138] Barnes and Tate)[139] pointed to the increased risk of isolation for people from BME communities in these settings, concluding that advocacy needs would be most appropriately met through specialist and appropriate BME provision.

Three papers (Chouhan and MacAttram;[140] Christie and Hill;[141] Watters)[142] describe advocacy as an integral element of ACMHS, being provided by workers as part of a wider role on behalf of clients and families. Chouhan and MacAttram's[143] survey of 30 organisations identified 12 from the 25 returns that were providing advocacy as a range of mental health services including support to carers and families; practical assistance; housing advice; support with psychological/emotional issues; medication assistance; early intervention; and counselling. All of the studies identify grass-roots credentials and skills as essential in engaging with African and Caribbean communities. This is confirmed by the study by Platzer and Foley,[144] which includes a case study of advocacy provision by an African and Caribbean organisation. The service employed 17 staff, 3 (that is, 17%) of which were specifically employed as advocates, but the organisation estimated that in reality 65% of their time was spent on advocacy.

The location of services in the African and Caribbean community not only determines the identity of the organisation but also affects the approach to advocacy. Watters[145] draws on Sassoon and Lindow's work[146] and the distinction between 'reactive' and 'innovative' models of empowerment, describing a reactive approach that focuses on the impact of inequality in contrast to an innovative approach that is:

Table 4
Quality appraisal and strength of evidence

Advocacy provision	Study details	Evidence type	Quality appraisal	Strength of evidence in relation to the review question
African and Caribbean mental health advocacy	Chouhan and MacAttram[124]	Descriptive survey of African and Caribbean mental health services.	Method for data collection clear; findings clear but more detail on analysis could have been provided. Accessible with clear recommendations and a summary of evidence for them.	Medium
	Christie and Hill[125]	Descriptive – user-led research involving service visits.	Largely a description of project visits and the common themes from these. Light on design and no detail on method of analysis. Descriptions of different projects serves to highlight how they work. The report is well presented and accessible.	Medium
	Watters[126]	Descriptive paper of evaluative study.	Focused on one African and Caribbean service, detail on method or analysis. Further material relating to evaluation study not found. Information about advocacy specifically limited and therefore utility low.	Low

Table 4 continued

Advocacy provision	Study details	Evidence type	Quality appraisal	Strength of evidence in relation to the review question
BME mental health advocacy	Rai-Atkins et al[127]	Descriptive – service including case studies capturing user and service views and experience.	Mix of methods but difficulties with recruitment of participants. Little detail regarding analysis. Messages are clearly articulated but the relationship between the recommendations and the findings is not always clear.	Medium

Table 4 continued

Advocacy provision	Study details	Evidence type	Quality appraisal	Strength of evidence in relation to the review question
Generic mental health advocacy	Platzer and Foley[128]	Mixed method involving mapping of mental health need and provision; survey of mental health advocacy organisations'; focus groups with stakeholders and case studies.	This study is of good quality. It would be strengthened by further detail on the methods used for analysis of focus group and case study material. The method for mapping service provision is the focus of a separate paper.[129] The messages are clear. It is not clear whether the findings would be generalisable outside of the London context.	Medium

Table 4 continued

Advocacy provision	Study details	Evidence type	Quality appraisal	Strength of evidence in relation to the review question
Generic mental health advocacy	Mind[130]	Descriptive survey involving consultations with over 150 service users, including African and Caribbean men.	These standards were developed through extensive involvement with service users, including African and Caribbean men. The use of a broader range of approaches to collect evidence systematically appeared to be outwith the terms of reference for the project. There is little detail on analysis of the findings and the link between the evidence base and the recommendations is not made explicit.	Medium

Table 4 continued

Advocacy provision	Study details	Evidence type	Quality appraisal	Strength of evidence in relation to the review question
Generic mental health advocacy	McKeown et al[131]	Mixed method process evaluation involving an analysis of data sheets and case data files for client contacts and collection of the views of stakeholders using semi-structured interviews.	The study is relevant to the review question although restricted to secure settings. It explains its aims and method but lacks detail on analysis and theoretical frameworks. The sample and methods of fieldwork are appropriate although other methods of capturing data on outcomes could have been considered. It is clearly written although findings could be more clearly presented.	Medium

Table 4 continued

Advocacy provision	Study details	Evidence type	Quality appraisal	Strength of evidence in relation to the review question
Generic mental health advocacy	Coleman et al[132]	Descriptive survey including questionnaire to service users, carers and professionals, interviews and focus group with service users.	This study is solely concerned with Sheffield. It does not provide information on sampling of stakeholders or participants or data analysis. No apparent theoretical framework. This is relatively accessible, aimed at a lay audience. The reporting of the results is rather confusing.	Weak
	Barnes and Tate[133]	Qualitative study involving interviews with service users, advocacy staff and mental health staff and managers.	Study to evaluate impact but does not analyse in terms of ethnic differences. The method and findings are clearly presented. The study would have been strengthened by additional outcome measures. Accessibility limited by length of report although broken down into four sections.	Weak

... not so much focused on the interaction with psychiatric services but provide a safe place around which consciousness around Black identity and its relationship to the psychiatric experience can be explored.[147]

Watters found that the development worker in his study of a specific service adopted both models, providing advocacy and working at an individual level on improving the relationship with mental health services and also working at a collective level to enable people to reflect on and strengthen their identity.

All of the studies focused on mental health advocacy draw attention to the importance of choice, cultural sensitivity and understanding as essential characteristics of advocacy for BME communities. The importance of shared cultural heritage and Black identity gains a stronger emphasis in those studies that focused on BME communities and they point to the 'colour-blindness' of mainstream services. Rai-Atkins et al[148] found that the only difference acknowledged by mainstream service providers was skin colour but otherwise the needs of BME communities were viewed as interchangeable with those of the White population. Further they found that most BME service users felt most empowered when they had an advocate reflecting their culture, gender and ethnicity. They concluded that there are five themes that advocacy services need to understand and address to be culturally competent: identity, faith, racism, gender and spirituality.

Christie and Hill[149] reflect that the combination of a clear Black identity, 'seeped in blackness', combined with professionalism, creates a safe space for African and Caribbean people with mental health problems who are otherwise at serious risk of exclusion. Chouhan and MacAttram[150] point to the importance of Black organisations employing Black staff that understand the social, cultural and political experiences of African and Caribbean mental health service users, concluding that it cannot be emphasised enough. Platzer and Foley[151] identify a style of advocacy called personal advocacy from one of the African and Caribbean services in their study. This style of advocacy goes beyond professional or instructed advocacy and is combined with support, befriending, access to counselling, mental health advocacy, advocacy in relation to general heath, and housing and benefits.

4.1.3 The impact of mental health advocacy

Information about the impact of advocacy was largely derived from the views of service users and staff, including advocacy providers, and to a lesser extent families and carers. These included the potential for advocacy to secure basic rights; create choice; improve the identification and understanding of mental health needs; promote self-advocacy and involvement in decision making; challenge discrimination; and promote access to complementary ways of healing and practical help. Both Barnes and Tate[152] and McKeown et al[153] identify how advocacy has helped individuals, for example, through providing information, giving the person a voice and raising awareness of rights. Similarly the advocacy needs assessment by Coleman et al[154] identified situations where it was thought advocacy would be of greatest benefit – welfare benefits, care programme approach (CPA) meetings, making complaints, talking to mental health professionals and housing issues. However, in none of these studies was the data analysed in terms of ethnicity.

Platzer and Foley[155] found that BME service users using personal advocacy reported greater benefits in terms of improvements in overall well-being and circumstances than for instructed advocacy. They found that this model of advocacy provision did cost more per case but was perhaps the most cost-effective method, as it was the most likely method to increase capacity for user involvement and empowerment.

4.1.4 Service users' experiences

In the studies by Watters[156] and Christie and Hill,[157] the importance of shared African and Caribbean identity was stressed by service users. This means:

- being able to communicate from the same standpoint, in the same linguistic and cultural terms;
- acknowledging and involving the family (a foundation for Black communities);
- recognising the psycho-social basis for mental distress and therefore that psycho-social interventions are important;

- recognising and acknowledging the effects of racism both internally for the individual and externally;
- understanding the importance of Black history and religious and spiritual beliefs.

Further, Christie and Hill[158] point to how a shared identity serves both to engage people and to increase the motivation of those services to help. Rai-Atkins et al[159] found a lack of confidence that White-dominated mainstream services could ever appropriately serve the African and Caribbean community.

In McKeown et al's study,[160] service users expressed a preference for an advocate of the same cultural heritage; however, the Mind inquiry[161] reported that the majority of Black Caribbean service users in their study valued respect and results more highly than cultural identification.

4.1.5 The process and implementation of advocacy

The factors identified for implementation of mental health advocacy centre around the design and provision of culturally appropriate service. While Christie and Hill[162] stress the importance of creating organisations with a sense of Black identity, they emphasise the need to work in partnership with other organisations including the statutory sector. Watters[163] describes the development of a service for African and Caribbean people with a serious mental illness. The service, which included advocacy as a function, was initially explicitly for this group. It was subsequently reorganised to become a more generic service. This had a significant negative impact on the engagement of African and Caribbean communities. Chouhan and MacAttram[164] found that the support, empowerment and culturally appropriate services offered by community organisations where an individual could identify with the staff, facilitates engagement with statutory services.

Rai-Atkins et al[165] highlight the need for a proactive community development approach to personal advocacy that reflects the dual functions of advocacy for BME communities, supporting the individual and community advocacy. The aim is to 'create culturally appropriate structures, enabling communities to identify and take control of the development of new services'. This theme of community-based action and engagement resonates with the SCMH study[166] and the study by Platzer and Foley.[167]

Finally, the issues relating to the fragility of funding for the BVCS that will inevitably affect the quality and sustainability of provision are highlighted by a number of the studies. Chouhan and MacAttram[168] identified that PCTs, local authorities and social services are the most common sources of funding with social services funding perceived to be the least secure, often lasting only a year with no guarantee of continuation. Adequate long-term core funding was consequently identified as the best way of sustaining the BVCS and Chouhan and MacAttram[169] suggested that funding on a long-term basis – a minimum of three or five years – would alleviate the pressures on BVCS and enable a strategic approach to their work. This would clearly not only support developments of advocacy provision but also the broader participation of service users and organisations in the development and monitoring of mental health service provision. The need for capacity building was also identified by Chouhan and MacAttram,[170] and this included fundraising; evaluation tools, human resources, management tools and business development and advice and comprehensive training.

4.1.6 Organisation of advocacy

All of the studies indicate a need for culturally sensitive provision. The studies focused on BME communities indicate that this needs to be culturally specific. The value of advocacy provision being interdependent with other aspects of provision is highlighted by Watters,[171] Christie and Hill,[172] Rai-Atkins et al[173] and Platzer and Foley.[174] McKeown et al[175] identify the benefits of providing culturally specific advocacy within a secure setting through arrangements with appropriate organisations. However, Platzer and Foley[176] found that access to community-oriented schemes were harder to access once service users were admitted to hospital.

4.2 Descriptions of advocacy provision for African and Caribbean men

The richest source of information about mental health advocacy for African and Caribbean communities is from the grey literature and service descriptions that have been specifically developed to meet the needs of African and Caribbean communities. Thirty-nine service reports were identified, either via the web or in response to requests made as part of the practice survey. These reports relate to 37 services, 7 were excluded because they either made no reference to the provision of advocacy or did not provide mental health advocacy. Thirty service reports were analysed in detail. The detail and quality of this information varied enormously, from a leaflet aimed at service users and professionals, briefly describing the organisation, range of provision and access, to Annual Reports and in one instance a video. In addition 6 papers, including one referring to one of the projects, were identified through the search that provided a description of a service consistent with the inclusion criteria for the review. As these dated from 1996, it is possible that there have been significant changes in the services described.

An overview of the different types of services is provided in Table 4 and a summary of the data extracted from these reports and papers is available online at www.scie.org.uk/publications/knowledgereviews/ kr15-appendices.pdf. This is, of course, a limited source of data and does not capture the richness of advocacy activity in any of these organisations. As can be seen there is a reasonable geographical spread, with 36% of the information relating to services in London and 5% to national provision. Information on African and Caribbean organisations accounts for 28%, BME organisations 25%, mental health advocacy services 30% and generic advocacy services 17%.

4.2.1 Needs for advocacy

The service descriptions highlighted a broad range of needs for advocacy for African and Caribbean men. In rank order of frequency these were:

- over-representation in mental health services;
- insufficient support in the community across statutory and voluntary sectors;
- difficulties in communication, which reinforce isolation;
- access to housing;
- support around benefits;
- complaints about statutory services;

Table 5
Summary of service descriptions analysed

Organisational focus	Number of services	Location
African and Caribbean mental health advocacy	2	2 London
African and Caribbean mental health	8	1 Manchester 1 Wolverhampton 1 Birmingham 1 Sheffield 3 London 1 National
BME generic advocacy	1	1 National
BME mental health advocacy	3	1 Leicester 1 Liverpool 1 London
BME mental health	5	1 Bradford 1 Bristol 1 Cardiff 2 London
Mental health advocacy	11	1 Bradford 1 Hampshire 1 Kent 1 Leeds 1 Northern Ireland 1 South Wales 1 Surrey 4 London
Generic advocacy	6	1 Flintshire 1 Staffordshire 1 Lancashire 2 Kent 1 London

- lack of economic and political power;
- medication issues;
- drug abuse;
- cultural needs ignored.

4.2.2 Advocacy provision

Mental health advocacy for African and Caribbean men is rarely provided as a stand-alone activity. There were slightly more examples of this for BME mental health advocacy services, some of which like Akwaaba Ayeh are open to BME groups but focus on provision to African and Caribbean communities. The majority of the services providing mental health advocacy with African and Caribbean men do so in the context of providing other services that are designed to enable them to address their mental health problems. These services include accommodation, employment or educational-related activities, support groups, befriending or counselling. For example, ACMHS in Manchester[177] describe providing advocacy alongside counselling, employment and training opportunities and a primary care mental health team. The literature for some of these services, for example, Family Health Isis,[178] make it clear that advocacy and associated mental health provision has developed from concern about shortfalls in mainstream service provision and the negative experiences, including compulsory detention, of African and Caribbean men in relation to mental health services.

Few of the mental health advocacy services mentioned provision to African and Caribbean, or wider BME communities. One notable exception was Mind in Haringuey, which has established a dedicated African and Caribbean advocacy service managed by a wider mental health advocacy service. Two other advocacy services included information about provision to BME communities, Bromley Mental Health Advocacy Project[179] and Brent Advocacy Concerns.[180]

Across all organisational types, the majority of advocacy provided was individual casework and the service descriptions identified the following, again in order of frequency:

- representation at ward rounds and/or CPA meetings;
- benefits and housing advice;
- access to appropriate services and alternative forms of help;

- rights under the Mental Health Act and/or access to legal representation;
- employment and training opportunities;
- representing views at management meetings;
- empowering individuals to self-advocate;
- providing information about a range of services/entitlements;
- making a complaint;
- staff training;
- immigration problems;
- acting as appropriate adult;
- liaising with children's services;
- tackling abuse and discrimination;
- general health.

Advocacy in hospital settings is mentioned by many of the organisations, particularly mental health organisations, with some such as the National Alliance for Mental Health in Northern Ireland[181] citing resource constraints as limiting their activity. Provision in other contexts was referred to, particularly community settings such as community mental health teams and day centres with also forensic and prison settings.

Group or collective advocacy was mentioned by approximately half of the African and Caribbean organisations with the description of Simba[182] providing rich detail of this in practice. The broadest range of advocacy described was for those services that provide advocacy with other clients as well as those with mental health problems. Citizen advocacy and peer advocacy are mentioned most often by generic advocacy services, although it is often unclear whether these have been developed for mental health clients, or are being used predominantly with other clients, specifically those with a learning disability.

In Figure 2, the different types of advocacy providers are mapped against the conceptual framework adapted from Carlisle's work, in order to locate and identify differences in the type of advocacy provided by different organisational arrangements.

4.2.3 Outcomes

Although many of the project reports had a clear description of what they were trying to achieve, almost without exception, they provide a description of activity or process rather than outcomes. One report provided outcomes for a small number of African and Caribbean advocacy partners, while another provided a description of how it had succeeded in making a difference to one man's life. The advocacy goals identified by African and Caribbean services were framed in terms of the negative experiences of mental health services and unmet need for African and Caribbean communities.

Figure 2
Advocacy service descriptions mapped
against dimensions of advocacy

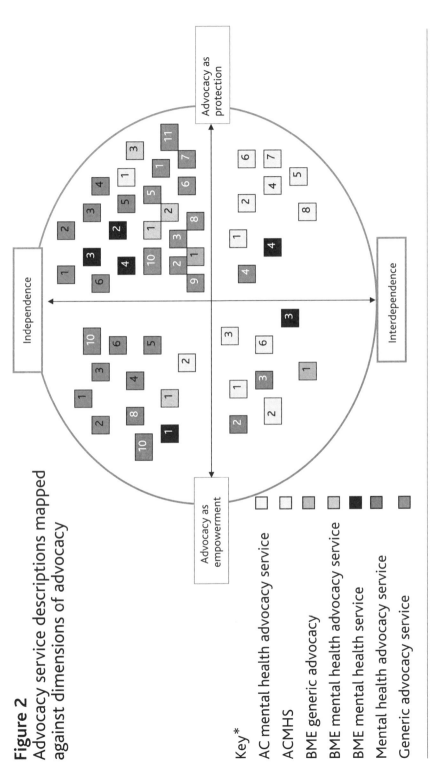

Key*

☐ AC mental health advocacy service

☐ ACMHS

▨ BME generic advocacy

▨ BME mental health advocacy service

■ BME mental health service

▨ Mental health advocacy service

▨ Generic advocacy service

* The numbers for each of the different services refers to a specific service description, detailed online at www.scie.org.
uk/publications/knowledgereviews/kr15-appendices.pdf

5

Discussion

5.1 Limitations of the Research Review

The major limitation is the lack of evidence relevant to the review question. In part this reflects the limited capacity within the organisations concerned to evaluate, publish and disseminate accounts of their work. This difficulty meant that we broadened our methodology to include a thematic analysis and conceptual mapping of indirectly relevant material.

Time and resources also limited the involvement of African and Caribbean men and organisations as stakeholders in this review. In particular their involvement in the more technical aspects of the Knowledge Review needed to be supported by capacity building and the Social Care Institute for Excellence (SCIE) should consider how to address this in future commissions.

5.2 Current models of mental health advocacy provision for African and Caribbean men

This review has indicated there is a diversity of organisational arrangements for the provision of mental health of advocacy with African and Caribbean men. This function can be delivered as a separate service or embedded within other services and it can be focused on particular ethnic or client groups or organised around broader ethnic groups and across different client groups. ACMHS have clearly developed in response to concerns about the failure of mainstream mental health services to meet the needs of African and Caribbean men. The approach to advocacy developed by BVCS is qualitatively different and the interdependence with other aspects of provision provides a strategy for tackling social disadvantage associated not only with mental health status but also ethnic identity.

It is not clear to what extent local context – demographic profile, existing service provision, community and voluntary sector infrastructure, opportunities for development – influence arrangements for the provision of specialist advocacy for African and Caribbean men. However, in general, there was little evidence of a strategic approach to the development of mental health advocacy.

5.3 Features of best practice and factors influencing the provision of best practice in relation to the specific needs of the client group

There was a high degree of agreement from the different sources of knowledge that focused on African and Caribbean or BME communities as to what constituted good practice. The following were identified:

* Advocacy for African and Caribbean men needs to address the double discrimination of racism and mental illness experienced by BME communities.
* The provision of a safe and secure relationship within which the feelings of isolation and consequences of stigma associated with mental illness and racism can be addressed is a recurrent theme. This resonates with studies of the experience of African and Caribbean communities in relation to mental health services, both mainstream[183] and specialist.[184]
* The centrality and specificity of advocacy with the linguistic and cultural needs of BME groups in general and African and Caribbean men in particular. Underpinning these needs is a different world view that emphasises the promotion of health, reintegration of the self, connection to and development of the community, spirituality, self-knowledge, and oneness.[185]
* Adopting a proactive approach that ensures that those who are the most passive and/or least able to engage, as a result of mental illness or whose rights are at greatest risk of jeopardy are offered the opportunity to have an advocate.
* The centrality of choice, especially in terms of gender, and demonstrable ethnic sensitivity.
* Balancing accessibility and informality with professionalism to ensure that advocacy services are delivered to high standards.

- A well-trained, well-equipped and well-supported workforce.
- Partnership working and facilitated networking across sectors to encourage exchange of information, best practice and mutual understanding.
- Sustainability, with specific reference to funding.

5.4 The impact of different types of advocacy provision on individual and organisational outcomes

This review confirms the absence of studies considering the effectiveness of mental health advocacy as a significant knowledge gap. There is the suggestion from the study by Platzer and Foley[186] that BME communities prefer and derive greater benefit from personal advocacy. Whether this is restricted to BME communities is not clear. Indeed, a recent Australian[187] study comparing the effectiveness of routine rights advocacy with an experimental model of personal advocacy for people detained in hospital found that personal advocacy led to significant improvements in patients' and staff members' experience of voluntary treatment and compliance with after-care, resulting in a statistically and economically significant reduction in hospitalisation.

5.5 How should mental health advocacy be organised for African and Caribbean men?

The review provides evidence to support the provision of advocacy that is sensitive to the linguistic, cultural and social needs of African and Caribbean men. The two studies of secure services found that there was a need for culturally sensitive provision, and it was proposed that this could be organised and coordinated through a generic mental health advocacy service with a specific agreement with an appropriate BME organisation.

There were differing views on whether advocacy provision should be culturally specific. Two of the primary studies arrived at different conclusions in this regard: Rai-Atkins et al[188] found a preference for an advocate that reflected cultural background, language and gender while the Mind inquiry[189] found that Black Caribbean service users valued respect and results more highly than cultural identification. Further, Bowes and

Sim[190] found that membership of a BME group rather than specific heritage was important, as there were marked differences of experience and preferences within ethnic groups. It is worth noting, however, that none of these studies focused exclusively on the African and Caribbean community and the different findings may well reflect differences in the extent and engagement of communities, and possibly the ethnic affiliation of the researchers. There is also recognition that some men may want other types of specialist services. Ludwig[191] draws attention to the experience of Black gay men who identify by reference to their sexuality rather than by their race and access advocacy accordingly.

It is evident from the advocacy literature that there is an enthusiasm for professional, independent advocacy. This review has indicated that engagement and provision of advocacy with African and Caribbean men may be more successful if an approach to advocacy is adopted that looks beyond the relationship with mental health services and views advocacy as a strategy for achieving equality and strengthening identity. However, African and Caribbean men also clearly need access to professional advocacy, independent of statutory services, to safeguard their rights and support the effective management of their interaction with mental health services.

The review has identified a need for a strategic approach to the provision of mental health advocacy. This would need to establish the local demographic profile and the specific advocacy needs of the local population, as well as the available resources. However, there should be an emphasis on the development of a whole system of advocacy, facilitating partnership working across organisations to increase choice and access to a broader range of advocacy. The value of a strategic approach is confirmed by Barker et al[192] from an investigation into the characteristics of successful mental health advocacy projects. Their study did not have a specific BME focus but identified the importance of broad-based support and a sponsoring agency in ensuring the sustainability. In the absence of a strategic approach, there is a risk that mental health advocacy for African and Caribbean men may be ignored or marginalised.

6

Summary and conclusions

6.1   Gaps in knowledge

This Research Review has identified clear gaps in the evidence base. First, there has been no systematic inquiry into the different advocacy needs of African and Caribbean men. Second, the research on the mechanisms and outcomes of advocacy, for mental health service users in general and African and Caribbean men in particular, is limited. There appears to be an absence of research into advocacy models based on empowerment, although many of the project reports reviewed identified this as an aspiration. Further, there is no clear information on different approaches that can or should be used for different genders or age groups.

There have been no evaluations that directly compare the benefits of different ways of organising mental health advocacy for African and Caribbean men. Further, there does not currently exist an agreed set of advocacy standards as a basis for audit by different types of organisations, although Action 4 Advocacy's standards are increasingly being used and adopted.

6.2   Development of mental health advocacy for African and Caribbean men

Despite the gaps in research knowledge there is a significant amount of useful and positive information from a practitioner perspective to build on. The review has identified different models for the provision of advocacy reflecting, in part, different conceptualisations of the main functions of advocacy and identified key outcome areas. The predominant approach is professional independent advocacy whose main function is to protect the rights of mental health service users. However, the descriptions of ACMHS identified a broader role for advocacy. This is not solely predicated on changing the relationship with mental health

73

services but aims to address the broader basis of social exclusion and disadvantage faced by African and Caribbean men.

There is, however, agreement, from the diverse sources of evidence reviewed, that mental health advocacy needs to be culturally sensitive and responsive. This means a well-developed understanding of the needs of African and Caribbean men, their experience of racism, their culture and language, and the ways in which social disadvantage and social exclusion operate to perpetuate their difficulties. The evidence regarding the cultural specificity of advocacy provision is unclear, with the quality of the advocacy relationship, ability to deliver results and the differences within the same ethnic groups emerging as being as important as shared identity. However, this evidence comes from studies that have not been primarily designed to address this issue in relation to African and Caribbean men and is therefore weak.

The review has confirmed that in general, mental health advocacy services do not demonstrate a well-developed understanding of the advocacy needs of African and Caribbean men. The location of advocacy alongside other services for African and Caribbean communities facilitates engagement with advocacy and provides an advocacy relationship that is likely to offer continuity and be responsive to changing needs.

6.3   Implications for future studies

There is now a clear need for both quantitative and qualitative evaluations of the different models for advocacy provision in terms of process and outcomes. Griffiths[193] provides an illustration of developing an evaluation framework from the perspective of African and Caribbean men in relation to an arts project and both the process and outcome of this exercise have clear relevance to the evaluation of mental health advocacy for African and Caribbean men. This needs to be placed in a context of other forms of evaluation, and Rapaport et al[194] have recently provided an overview of the main models of evaluation for advocacy schemes in respect of people with learning disabilities.

6.4 Conclusion

The analysis of the provision of mental health advocacy for African and Caribbean men throws up some fundamental questions about the purpose and role of mental health advocacy. The current development of advocacy is focused on independent professional advocacy to ensure that rights are safeguarded. An analysis of the needs of African and Caribbean men indicate that while this focus is necessary it is not sufficient. Attention needs to be paid to enabling African and Caribbean men to tackle discrimination and exclusion on a broader front, not only in relationship with mental health services. This suggests that mental health advocacy needs to have a broader definiton and a conceptual framework has been developed to locate advocacy not only as a strategy for protection and empowerment but also for community engagement.

Practice Survey

7 Aims

This section of the report provides an overview of the Practice Survey, the methodology and findings. The aims of the Practice Survey were to:

1. Identify current organisational arrangements, current practice and the current challenges and opportunities that these organisations face in delivering the highest quality services to African and Caribbean men.
2. Explore the experiences of African and Caribbean men using specialist mental health services and their definition of best practice in the provision of advocacy to meet their needs.
3. Explore the experiences of African and Caribbean men using advocacy services and non-users of advocacy to identify their views of these services, the extent to which they are meeting their needs and to identify potential areas of development.
4. Explore the views of stakeholders including commissioners, providers of advocacy services and staff working in mental health services.

Methodology

8.1 Stakeholder involvement

The partnership approach to this Knowledge Review was described in Section 1.3. Specific to the Practice Survey, individuals from the partner organisations were involved in:

- the construction and refinement of the data collection tool for the survey of the advocacy organisations;
- the construction and refinement of interview and focus group schedules;
- designing and delivering training to undertake focus group facilitation;
- facilitating focus groups;
- interviewing for the case studies;
- commenting on the emergent findings and drafts of reports;
- undertaking some of the telephone interviews;
- construction and compilation of database

8.2 Sources of information

There were three elements to the Practice Survey. First, a survey of advocacy providers was undertaken to establish how advocacy is currently provided for African and Caribbean men. This utilised a purposive sampling approach, common to qualitative inquiry. This approach means that a sample is selected on the basis of particular characteristics to enable an in-depth exploration of the themes.[195] In this instance, respondents were selected on the basis of their potential to embody a different perspective or distinct organisational features from other responding organisations.

Second, focus groups were held with African and Caribbean men to determine the principles and preferred characteristics of advocacy services for those men experiencing mental health problems. Third, there were limited case studies to provide an in-depth understanding of how advocacy needs to be organised to provide high-quality and effective advocacy for African and Caribbean men.

8.2.1 Survey

The preliminary work included the following.

Construction and piloting of a data collection tool (online at www.scie. org.uk/publications/knowledgereviews/kr15-appendices.pdf). This covered:

- key principles
- current organisational arrangements
- resources available including staffing
- services provided including attention to services provided across different practice locations, ranging from police custody, in-patient care, and community care services
- equalities monitoring, specifically use of services by African and Caribbean men
- mechanisms for service user involvement
- arrangements for governance and quality assurance.

Construction and compilation of an advocacy organisations database. A total of 669 potential mental health advocacy providers to African and Caribbean men were identified through internet searching, the partner organisations and publicly available databases of advocacy services and mental health services for Black and minority ethnic (BME) communities, including African and Caribbean communities. After duplicates were removed, the following criteria developed from the terms of reference for the review were used to finalise the database:

Inclusion criteria

Services providing mental health advocacy for adults of working age that are either targeted at African and/or African and Caribbean men,

BME communities or provide a service for the whole population in a locality.

Exclusion criteria

- **Age**
  Older people
  Children

- **Type of advocacy**
  Not mental health advocacy
  Carers
  General disability

- **Ethnicity**
  Refugees and asylum seekers
  Targeted at ethnic groups, excluding African and Caribbean men

- **Gender**
  Women only

- **Organisation**
  Service provision other than advocacy or mental health
  Umbrella organisations that do not provide a direct service

Figure 3
Organisations potentially providing mental health advocacy for African and Caribbean men

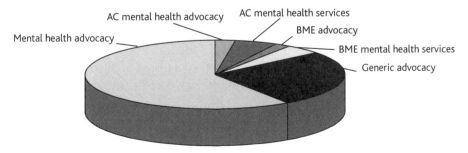

A total of 431 organisations were left. For 40 organisations it was not clear whether they provided advocacy; the remaining 391 were categorised using the typology that was developed to guide the sampling. This is available in Appendix 4 and Figure 3 provides an overview of the proportions of the different types of organisations in the database. It was not always clear to what extent community and social organisations went beyond providing information and advice and general advocacy to providing mental health advocacy. However, they make up 17% of the organisations on the database and represent an important resource and were included in the sample.

The majority of the organisations identified were in England. One BME mental health organisation providing advocacy was identified in Wales and none in Northern Ireland, although in both areas generic mental health advocacy is provided.

Data collection has proceeded via two stages:

- Stage one: email or postal contact with all organisations in database. This resulted in minimal returns, possibly because of a combination of time pressures on the potential respondents, changes to organisations and the length of the survey tool.
- Stage two: telephone contact ensuring a purposive sample of organisations using the typology in Appendix 4. The sample therefore included a range of organisations in three broad categories, namely African and/ or African and Caribbean-focused organisations, BME community-focused organisations and advocacy organisations. Fifty-two organisations participated and the breakdown of responses is summarised in Table 6.

We encountered a number of difficulties with the survey. First, a number of organisations identified through internet searches and existing databases no longer existed or their contact details had changed and it was not possible to retrieve them (6%). Second, either there was no response from the organisation or they declined to take part and this accounted for 25% of the 391 organisations identified. Capacity was clearly an issue, particularly for service user organisations with the majority declining to take part and also BME organisations, with a number of potential respondents indicating they had insufficient time to spend completing a telephone interview.

Table 6
Sample in the Practice Survey

Organisational type	Number of respondents (%)
African and Caribbean-focused	
African and Caribbean mental health advocacy	3 (6)
African and Caribbean mental health service	5 (9.5)
African and Caribbean service user group	0 (0)
African and Caribbean community organisation	7 (13.5)
Total	15 (29)
BME-focused	
BME mental health advocacy	4 (7.5)
BME mental health organisation	7 (13.5)
BME service user group	0 (0)
BME community organisation	3 (6)
Total	14 (27)
Advocacy-focused	
Generic advocacy	7 (13.5)
Mental health advocacy	15 (28.5)
Mental health user group	1 (2)
Total	23 (44)
Grand total	52 (100)

Organisations' published materials, including relevant reports and annual reports, were also requested and have been included for analysis in the research review element of the project.

8.2.2 Focus groups

In preparation for the focus groups and to enable men who use mental health services to facilitate the focus groups, training was provided over five weeks, lasting between one-and-a-half and three hours per session. An overview of this training is provided online at www.scie.org.uk/publications/knowledgereviews/kr15-appendices.pdf. Given the logistics of the focus groups, it proved practically impossible to include the men in all of the groups. In effect the training workshops functioned as focus groups, providing an in-depth understanding of both the issues that the men faced and what they would like from mental health advocacy. This information has been included in the analysis. These workshops had advantages over the focus groups as a relationship of trust clearly developed with the facilitator over the training sessions. Both the men individually and their organisations commented on how invaluable these workshops had been in developing confidence and strengthening ability to participate.

Four focus groups were held and the topic guide is available online at www.scie.org.uk/publications/knowledgereviews/kr15-appendices.pdf. They were designed to:

- examine what is meant by the term 'advocacy' with African and Caribbean men;
- share experiences, opinions, insights and views around what advocacy services mean to African and Caribbean men;
- explore access to and experience of advocacy;
- identify the principles and characteristics that African and Caribbean men view as critical in the delivery of specialist mental health advocacy;
- explore preferences for how mental health advocacy services should be organised to meet the diverse needs of African and Caribbean men.

Demographic information and information about mental health service use by African and Caribbean men from the Mental Health Minimum Dataset was used to identify sites for the focus groups. The locations that were originally selected differed in terms of the numbers of African and Caribbean men in contact with the services (high, medium and low) and different organisational arrangements (African and Caribbean, BME or advocacy-focused). However, it proved difficult to recruit men in areas where there were no community organisations for African and Caribbean men, and therefore areas where there was an organisation were selected. The most successful method for recruiting men was via these organisations and attempts at recruiting via NHS trusts were unsuccessful. In the final event, a total of 25 Black Caribbean, Black African and dual heritage men participated, ranging in age from early 20s to mid 40s. Only two of the men attending the focus groups had experienced independent mental health advocacy services. They did, however, have the experience of advocacy provided by members of staff working within African and Caribbean mental health services. Importantly, the men talked about the services they were currently receiving and how these were related to advocacy.

Seven support workers also attended the groups. In addition a consultation group was held attended by six men. The aim of this was to feed back the findings from the initial focus groups to further develop the themes.

Two of the focus groups had two facilitators, male and female, both African and Caribbean and two had one facilitator, both female, one African and Caribbean and one White. The consultation group was facilitated by an African and Caribbean man. The proceedings for three of the focus groups were taped and transcribed. Participants were paid out-of-pocket expenses and a small payment for their time and inconvenience, consistent with good practice.[196] The topic guide for the facilitation of the focus groups is provided online at www.scie.org.uk/publications/knowledgereviews/kr15-appendices.pdf.

8.2.3 Case studies

Three case studies were originally designed to provide an in-depth understanding of advocacy. These involved interviews with staff and service users in mental health services. Ethics committee approval was required. The process of securing this approval and subsequently fulfilling the requirements of the local research governance committee in one site was not compatible with the time and resources allowed for this project. It was therefore decided to undertake interviews with a broad range of stakeholders from different locations to develop the understanding of how advocacy works in practice for African and Caribbean men. The relevant interview schedules can be found in online at www.scie.org.uk/publications/knowledgereviews/kr15-appendices.pdf. In total, 22 people were interviewed including 7 service users, 6 commissioners, 4 mental health service providers and 5 experts in the field. The interviews covered:

- preferred definitions of advocacy;
- characteristics of high-quality effective services;
- factors that facilitated or hindered the development of mental health advocacy;
- support provided and the extent to which this met expressed needs;
- arrangements for monitoring and evaluating the effectiveness of the service provided and for service user involvement in these processes;
- detail on organisational arrangements.

8.3 Confidentiality and ethical issues

Informed consent in the context of this study means consent that is freely given with proper understanding of the nature and consequences of what is proposed.[197] The written informed consent of all mental health service users to take part in the research was required for inclusion.

Confidentiality in focus groups proved to be paramount for the participants, reflecting a mistrust of mental health services and research generally, and concerns that the research did not always accurately reflect their opinions and concerns. Attention was therefore paid to engaging the men on their own terms and this enabled the men to share personal and sensitive information. Any information was completely anonymised in the subsequent analysis of the data and the reporting of findings.

8.4 Data analysis

The qualitative interview, focus group data and material from project reports was analysed using systematic thematic content analysis. The analysis adhered to published criteria for qualitative research.[198] The information from individual organisations was anonymised.

9

Provision of mental health advocacy: different types of groups, different forms of advocacy

9.1 Provision of mental health advocacy

The Practice Survey indicates that mental health advocacy with African and Caribbean men is provided, or could potentially be provided, by a range of different organisations. The typology used to guide the data collection was further developed following data collection and Appendix 6 provides a description of the main characteristics of the different organisational arrangements. This makes it clear that there is substantial diversity in the provision of mental health advocacy that could be accessed by African and Caribbean men. The different organisational forms identified from the development of the database are:

- African and Caribbean-focused
  These are organisations geared to meet the needs of African and Caribbean communities. There are a range of groups set up for different purposes that are doing work that would be recognisable as advocacy. These are:
  > African and Carribbean mental health advocacy: operating as a stand-alone service or as a discrete element within a broader service that is usually a Black voluntary and community sector (BVCS) organisation but could also be a dedicated element of a generic mental health advocacy service;
  > African and Caribbean mental health services: providing advocacy as an integral part of wider culturally sensitive services;
  > African and Caribbean service user groups: providing collective and peer advocacy;
  > African and Caribbean community groups: these are constituted around social, recreational or advice, information and support

but may also provide an advocacy function. These groups may be targeted at specific African and Caribbean communities, sometimes tightly defined in relation to a particular ethnic origin, for example, the Congolese Community in London, or broadly open, for example, the African and Caribbean community in Kent.

- BME-focused
  These organisations are designed to meet the needs of diverse BME communities, including African and Caribbean, reflecting local demography. They include:
  > BME mental health advocacy services: as a stand-alone service or as a discrete element within a broader service. Within such services, referrals may be managed to ensure that partners are offered a choice of advocates, particular to the choice of an advocate of shared cultural background;
  > BME mental health services: providing advocacy as an integral part of wider culturally sensitive services;
  > BME service user groups;
  > BME community groups: similar to African and Caribbean community groups in terms of the range of function and activities but more widely targeted.

- Advocacy-focused
  Generic mental health advocacy services or generic advocacy services tend to be stand-alone services oriented to casework advocacy usually referred to as 'independent professional advocacy'. These organisations are potentially accessible by all local citizens and therefore do not formally exclude African and Caribbean men. They include:
  > mental health advocacy services: only provide advocacy for people with mental health problems and particularly those engaged with the mental health system;
  > generic advocacy services: advocacy of various forms that does not narrowly define its target group. So, mental health service users could have their advocacy needs met in the context of a service that also meets the needs of a range of disabilities other than mental health;

> mental health service user groups: who are constituted for broader information, support or campaigning activity and also get involved in individual advocacy but more commonly collective advocacy.

Appendix 7 provides illustrative examples of the different types of organisational arrangements. It is worth noting that little evidence was found of robust partnership arrangements between mental health advocacy organisations and BME-focused organisations, including those for African and Caribbean communities. Not surprisingly therefore, a number of respondents commented that the work of BVCS can be marginalised or appear to be segregated from mainstream provision.

9.2 Advocacy activity

While the emphasis on different types of advocacy activity varies between the different organisational forms, there was considerable overlap. In general the different organisations all provide the following:

- support in meetings with mental health services – ward rounds and care programme approach (CPA) meetings;
- representation – at mental health tribunals or as an Appropriate Adult;
- negotiation with service providers particularly in respect of medication and leave;
- signposting and referral to other sources of specialist support and support navigating the mental health system;
- working in partnership to enable partners to speak for themselves;
- supporting people to make complaints or air grievances;
- supporting people to access rights and entitlements.

In addition African and Caribbean and BME organisations were more likely to provide:

- interpretation and translation, particularly for African clients;
- help with housing and benefit issues;
- support for families;
- befriending.

While the ideal for advocacy is to achieve empowerment of the individual to advocate on their own behalf, the extent to which this can always be achieved depends on a number of factors and can change over time for any individual. In practice, substantial advocacy activity is led by the advocate and approximates to a representational form of advocacy. The location of advocacy therefore becomes important in terms of the extent to which it will facilitate access to other activities that enable personal development and empowerment. The location of advocacy in African and Caribbean, or BME mental health services facilitates access not only to advocacy but also to a range of other activities, many of which are designed to tackle the underlying causes of disadvantage.

9.3 Access to mental health advocacy by African and Caribbean men

Where an African and Caribbean focused organisation provides mental health advocacy, then more or less all of its clients will be African and Caribbean. The key issue is the extent to which all of the advocacy need is met by the provider organisations, particularly those where capacity is limited. The generic and mental health advocacy services and BME organisations have varying proportions of clientele drawn from African and Caribbean communities, reflecting in part the local demography or local provision of alternative advocacy services. For some of the BME organisations, African and Caribbean clients might make the largest use of services.

Many of the organisations did not formally monitor ethnicity or gender of their clients and therefore the data on uptake of advocacy by African and Caribbean men was limited. From the available data, there was a mixed picture in terms of proportions of African and Caribbean service users as a total of whole service use. The various BME advocacy and mental health service organisations ranged from one reporting 'very few' to the rest being between 25-90% African and Caribbean clients; typically the gender split would be reported as roughly fifty-fifty, but the organisation with the highest uptake suggested that the majority were women rather than men. It would appear, therefore, that African and Caribbean men make relatively reasonable use of these broader BME organisations. Many of these organisations will act on expressed need before considering the particular ethnicity of a prospective client. There is some evidence that non-Black clients are attracted to BVCS on the basis of reported quality, or in the absence of accessible alternatives locally.

There is a more mixed picture with regard to the mental health advocacy organisations, which might in part be explained by demographic variations. Nearly a third of the organisations had no system for monitoring ethnic data and, anecdotally, low numbers were reported. For those with monitoring systems, low proportional service use was reported by 25%, ranging from 0 to 2%, with one organisation having only ever seen one Black person for advocacy. A total of 25% reported rates of between 6-8% and the remaining 20%, all based in inner-city areas, reported between 18-25%. On the whole these figures were not disaggregated for gender.

Difficulties in engaging with African and Caribbean men were mentioned by a number of respondents from the different types of organisations. The identity of the organisation, outreach, the provision of other activities and the location of the service were all mentioned as ways of facilitating access. Indeed it was broadly felt that people needed to know about the range of possibilities for advocacy and where to get it if they were going to see any benefit. It is also worth noting that many of the men who participated in this study had been in-patients and as many of the respective units will have a relationship with an advocacy service it raises a fundamental question as to the extent that mental health services facilitate access to advocacy for African and Caribbean men.

What does advocacy mean?

10.1 The meaning of advocacy

For service users there was a range of appreciations of the concept of advocacy. Many service users initially said that they had not come across it and the term was clearly alien and unfamiliar, including individuals for whom the term had no meaning at all:

'Advocacy is a frightening word – don't understand it.… Should be another word that has a similar meaning … it could be "Sparring-P" – a friend who would defend you, would be there for you. You know how strong the person is and they fight for you – you get the person to stand up for you.'

Other people identified advocacy as part of the role of staff in mental health services, both mainstream and those provided by the BVCS – to support clients and aid recovery. Service users also reported a range of other key people who provided advocacy-like support (notably these would include family members or religious pastors), and help from established groups such as a Citizens Advice Bureau.

A small number of service users had experienced mental health advocacy services, and as noted above this might have been organised in a number of ways by differently constituted services. Service users had well-developed ideas about self-advocacy, and agreed this ought to be the goal that people aspire to. This advocacy principle was linked in the minds of some service users to their cultural identity, in which self-reliance and the need 'to stand on your own two feet' had been instilled.

Initial wariness regarding the word 'advocacy' tended to diminish in focus group discussions, with people becoming more comfortable with it and on occasion using it themselves. When offered a brief outline of the sort of things encompassed by a notion of advocacy, participants more often than not recognised at least some of these elements as meaningful to their own experiences. For example, they would recognise advocacy in the role of staff concerned with their individual care and have an appreciation of collective advocacy as a mechanism for improving mental health services for African and Caribbean service users. The fact that for many there was an initial lack of awareness of advocacy, what it might be and its availability, has implications for access to and uptake of advocacy.

For services providing mental health advocacy or specialist Black mental health services the notion of advocacy was usually expressed in terms of guiding principles or service philosophy. This was usually articulated around key principles of advocacy, empowerment and partnership. These principles included commitments to promoting rights and entitlements and to exploring choices. Many described the advocacy role as assisting the person to have their voice heard, in circumstances often antithetical to this end. Independence was also emphasised, particularly for generic mental health advocacy services.

Some respondents also chose to define what advocacy was not. In this sense, advocacy was not about 'telling you what to do or say', 'guessing what you think' or 'counselling, therapy or advice'.

The advocate could be seen as a negotiator/mediator, a person to go in and sort problems out, act as a go-between, or support someone to make their own case. These approaches were not mutually exclusive, and advocates would assume different roles dependent on expressed wishes or circumstances. The ultimate goal would be that individuals were empowered to speak for themselves.

The community and collective nature of the BVCS in this sample leads to a holistic view of advocacy. Within this, the role of the advocate is to help the client get to where they are going and this cannot be done in isolation to their other needs. Advocacy is, hence, seen as part of a collective meeting of other needs. This is usually expressed in tandem with a strong commitment to equality goals. A number of generic mental health advocacy services also espoused broad objectives of promoting social inclusion, equality and social justice. Holistic or social models of mental health are presented as an alternative to rigid biomedical approaches that are seen as distinctly disadvantageous for Black men. This is often then translated into ways of working that appear as forms of collective advocacy.

Some service users emphasised the politics of race in mental health services, and wished for advocacy that was collectivised and politicised, arguing for fundamental changes to services and legislation – advocacy 'with teeth'. This could be associated with a community-based service with an organic understanding of 'roots', culture and history, appreciative of the role of discrimination and racism in people's experiences of mental health problems.

The awareness of advocacy among the small number of mainstream service provider staff was variable. The confusion about the professional role vis-à-vis advocacy was evident, as has been documented elsewhere.[199] This was often coupled, however, with upset at criticism of mainstream services emanating from advocacy groups and an indication that staff in mainstream mental health services are critical of advocacy and BME groups on their patch:

> '... advocacy is seen as an enemy ... as interfering. African and Caribbean men are expected to comply – advocacy rocks the nursing boat.'

The independence of voluntary sector groups was also questioned, with the view expressed that they appeared on occasion to be advocating for their organisation rather than individual client's needs.

10.2 The need for advocacy

Regardless of whether service users had had direct experience of advocacy or not, there was a broad consensus on the pressing need for advocacy. This might be framed in terms of numerous issues borne out of the experiences of African and Caribbean men in mental health services, for which effective advocacy would be seen to be beneficial. The majority of service users were critical of mainstream mental health services, and reported the sort of negative experiences and perceptions that have been widely reported elsewhere.[200] These views were not unremitting, however, and positive experiences of mainstream mental health services were also reported, albeit a minority view.

The following issues emerged as particularly pertinent to advocacy:

- a range of negative experiences of medication and side-effects, including lack of involvement in prescribing decisions, and a feeling that medication is more heavily prescribed than for White peers;
- lack of access to alternative treatments, especially talking therapies;
- physical confrontations and manhandling with an assumption from staff that African and Caribbean men are implicitly more aggressive or dangerous;
- misinterpretations of behaviour and not being allowed to behave in certain ways;
- limited opportunities to have one's experiences valued, especially if these are associated with cultural dimensions;
- limited opportunities for thorough engagement with community peers and community activities;
- involvement of the police and courts in admission into care, and greater likelihood of detention in locked wards or units with lengthier admission periods.

The majority of African and Caribbean participants in the Practice Survey were overwhelmingly critical of medication practices in mainstream services and this was often linked with broader dissatisfaction with a medical model of care. It was suggested that this was one of the most important areas of contention, where advocacy was both needed and could potentially make a difference. In one example, a service user reported taking medication for over 20 years but only the recent intervention of an advocate enabled him to negotiate dose reductions to a level that reduced his side-effects, helping him to cope and function better.

Staff in mainstream services felt that part of the need for independent Black organisations was to raise institutional awareness of cultural needs and to improve knowledge of both advocacy and the experiences of men from BME communities in mental health services. A dimension of this was the need to challenge racism in services:

'Racism is endemic in the system and it is reflected in staff attitudes, the way people talk to people. "I'm white, you're black – do what I say, take this". It also happens in reverse with white patients and black staff.'

10.3 Men, masculinity and mental health

There is a perceived reluctance for African and Caribbean men with mental health problems to acknowledge and/or talk about mental health problems. While trust is clearly an issue, this also appears to be associated with stigma within communities and possible notions of threatened masculinity.

> 'The challenge for advocacy services and Black men is finding them – a lot more Black men with mental health issues, but not picking them up.'

These issues emerged as most pertinent to young men. African and Caribbean women make more use of advocacy than their male counterparts, whether using culturally specific advocacy or specialist mental health services, or generic advocacy services. The gender of the advocacy worker might be important in this regard:

> 'I would prefer a man. I'm a shy guy about certain things that I can't talk to women about.'

With regard to stigma, the location of the service was very important:

> 'The good thing is that we are community-based, and the bad thing is that we are community-based.'

One service made a conscious decision to be based on the edge of town, away from the highest concentration of its target population, for these reasons.

A medical model, perceived to be over-reliant on high dosages of debilitating medication and services operating with implicit stereotypes of Black masculinity (associated with physicality, violence and aggression) are seen as a particularly invidious mix for African and Caribbean men admitted to care. A member of staff from a mainstream service drew attention to implicitly racialised undertones to expectations of client passivity in their relationship with care:

'People are just expected to be compliant, to be concordant and, to be white I suppose.'

Staff in one BME advocacy service suggested that for many African and Caribbean men mainstream mental health services could be thought of as the new form of slavery where 'medication is like the shackles and the whip'.

Advocates face scenarios where African and Caribbean men are reluctant to seek help for mental health problems because of perceived stigma. They can feel racially oppressed within services and suffer serious side-effects of sexual dysfunction associated with neuroleptic medication. This is a recipe for undermining positive ideas of self and masculinity, with treatment quite literally having emasculating effects. These particular needs go to the heart of the issue of trust in the advocacy relationship, further making the case for the value of advocacy and reinforcing the need for advocates with a shared background.

11

Respect and trust: the advocacy relationship

11.1 An advocate like me

The desirability of being able to choose an advocate from a shared cultural background was expressed across the board, by service users, staff working in the range of advocacy services or specialist mental health services. Choice was a recurring theme. For some men this might mean choosing an advocate from outside of their immediate community because of concerns to preserve privacy and confidentiality.

Generic mental health advocacy workers suggested that a lack of BME advocates might explain low uptake of advocacy by service users from BME communities. A number had consequently made appointments of appropriate advocacy staff on these grounds. In some instances this raised the issue of demands placed on a Black advocate within a generic service, who may wish to be recognised primarily as an advocate, meeting the needs of all prospective partners, rather than be seen as the 'Black' advocate.

Safety, trust and credibility were general issues that would define one's relationship with advocacy. Some service users felt they had learnt to mistrust workers within mental health establishments and therefore that they could only trust African and Caribbean people. They emphasised that advocates could only be respectful and useful if they were culturally sensitive or shared the same cultural background:

> 'The key question is how can you go to somebody for help if they don't respect you so the advocacy is an important thing.… If I don't feel safe, I am not going to go … I am not going to go to somebody else I will stay in the house and I will get worse.'

'I think it is very important … to go to a place where there are like-minded people of the same colour going through similar problems as yourself and you don't feel alone and you feel like you can communicate to certain people with regards to certain things which maybe very personal to you at that time.'

The visibility of Black staff within an organisation becomes immediately important. Arguably, service users need to see people who they can identify with:

'Black staff at [named organisation] can be seen right through the organisation from management to support workers.'

The importance of insider knowledge was also stressed. For example, the issue of cultural knowledge around spirituality, specifically, Rastafarianism was mentioned. Others spoke of the need for advocates to be 'streetwise'. On a more practical level, related aspects of choice focus on the provision of advocacy in a shared discourse, whether in terms of particular languages, patois or colloquialisms. This raised the need for either bilingual advocates or appropriate translation and interpreting services.

Some counterpoint positions, from commissioners and a minority of respondents from the BVCS, emphasised the hazards of marginalisation and a preference for mainstreaming. On the one hand, the need for distinct and bespoke services targeting specific minority ethnic groups was justified, pragmatically, on the basis of current and historical inadequacies in mainstream mental health services. However, some workers in Black community organisations highlighted the fact that this positioning might forever entrench outsider status and continue to locate Black people at the margins, possibly while the problems in mainstream services were left relatively untouched. In this sense the requirement for specialist services was to be resisted:

'[I] Feel that organisations like ours shouldn't have to keep making the case for alternative BME services. [I] suspect that many people still don't accept this. I wish that we didn't have to exist. All the services should be on the ball, but they're not and that's why we exist.'

A minority of service user participants in the focus groups were unconcerned about the ethnicity or the gender of any advocate but agreed that shared experience as users of services was important. In practical terms, service users wanted their advocates to be good, assertive negotiators, especially in terms of decisions about medication and transitions through services. Some expressed a preference for advocates to have a broad range of expertise rather than being a specialist in any one area. The ability to listen and hear, alongside a thorough understanding of the community, individual needs and mental health, was emphasised.

11.2 Relationships

The positive disposition towards advocacy was expressed in terms of the quality and value placed on the advocacy relationship: it really mattered that the worker 'knows us really well'. Despite it not being a primary aim of advocacy per se, some advocate respondents spoke of friendship and connectedness issues, often related to shared ethnicity. The importance of relationships with the person who would be one's advocate is illustrated in concerns about turnover among staff. When a new worker was assigned, 'you have to get to know them, to trust them ... if you can trust, it makes you feel better'. This is relevant for the organisation of advocacy. Formal, case-led, advocacy services, however, are often set up to offer more time-limited advocacy interventions, which militate against the development and sustaining of relationships. They also, depending on particular service configurations or commissioning arrangements, have difficulty in following cases across sectors, most obviously the transition between hospital and community-based care.

Associated with the value placed on relationships was an expressed desire for the advocate or key worker to make some sort of connection at the human level – and again the importance of a shared identity and 'belonging to the community' was stressed. While shared culture might be necessary it is not sufficient and there has to be a recognisable interest in people for themselves. Insincerity or falseness is easily recognised and adds to distress. This personal connection was seen to be in contrast to feelings of objectification and impersonal treatment within mainstream mental health services.

12

Results: the outcomes of advocacy

Achieving positive outcomes and the systematic monitoring of outcomes are seen to be crucial for demonstrating the value of advocacy. Desired outcomes were often articulated in terms of fairness and justice for individuals. Advocacy providers also described collective outcomes and strategies for achieving these. For example, better quality care plans and the extent of an individual's involvement in them might be better realised collectively than on a case-by-case basis. Similarly, more effective working partnerships across a range of agencies would be a positive consequence of forms of collective advocacy.

African and Caribbean and BME mental health advocacy providers often went beyond a narrow view of advocacy in pursuit of broader outcomes, often framed in terms of relationships, recovery and social inclusion. Service users report that such holistic support alleviates loneliness and supports greater independence. For them, the advantage of these services and their preference for them is that they foster a 'oneness' with each other. Individuals are able to express themselves in 'language they don't have to explain, or feel ashamed of or judged by'. For some men, the most important outcome is that they are able to get out of the house and meet with other users and like-minded people with African and Caribbean services offering a place of familiarity, safety and reassurance.

African and Caribbean organisations emphasised diverting men to less restrictive forms of care, keeping them out of hospital and out of mental health services as a key outcome. Box 1 provides an example that one service provided to illustrate this. This organisation estimated that about 20 hours per month of an advocate's time was spent on this alone, working with roughly three clients per month to achieve this. Other organisations claimed successes in negotiating discharge from hospital for people who felt they had been there too long. Similarly, they reported assisting people to negotiate reductions in medication. These interventions were deemed to be very successful, with the advocate stating that they knew about the range of positive outcomes because of sustained relationships with particular clients and being able to observe changes in the actions of service providers at first hand.

Other respondents described outcomes in terms of individual case issues and the work undertaken to achieve them. These would demonstrate the large range of issues that are brought forward by clients seeking the support of advocates. In this regard, positive outcomes would include accessing appropriate sources of assistance. More specifically, the outcome might be a specific adjustment to an aspect of a person's care, changes in the behaviour or attitude of a member of staff or the successful conclusion of a complaint or grievance.

Advocates were often at pains to make it clear that, although their work might necessarily involve supporting individuals to make complaints, they did not see this as a major part of their involvement with clients. In this regard they would stress a negotiation or mediation role, which might result in a compromise solution (see Box 1).

Comments were made on the link between successful outcomes and the extent to which the advocate could garner personal respect from staff, management and teams.

> '… need to earn their respect. It is not easy. But need respect to get outcomes for the patient.'

Because of both culturally specific issues and the context of negative experiences of African and Caribbean men, staff may need to be thoroughly informed by the advocate of the particular issues at stake – **this point alone suggests a profound difference in the advocacy role from that practised in generic contexts on behalf of the majority ethnic group with staff who share that ethnicity**.

Across all the different types of services there was a strong emphasis on outcomes being defined in terms of the personal goals set by the advocacy partner. However, it seems that as outcome data was rarely collected by services, individual stories remain the main source of information about positive results, with a widespread absence of a systematic and objective means of accounting for outcomes arising from advocacy. This lack of outcome measurement was often attributed to the pressures of providing a service.

Box 1
Diverting African and Caribbean men to less restrictive care

A Black African and Caribbean man was detained at a high secure hospital. After he had been there several years it was agreed that he had sufficiently recovered to be transferred to a regional medium secure unit, thus making it easier for family contact. This would also enable community links to be established prior to his eventual discharge.

The mental health tribunal 12 months previously had agreed to community visits locally, in preparation for his transfer to the medium secure unit. It was essential that he be assessed outside the hospital setting with the necessary security arrangements prior to his transfer.

The African and Caribbean Mental Health Service (ACMHS) had been supporting the client and his family. As a result, the ACMHS made representation on his behalf. The hospital could not give a reasonable explanation for not carrying out the previous recommendations. Following intervention by the ACMHS, arrangements were made for the man to have community visits and he was subsequently transferred to the medium secure unit making it easier for family and friends to visit.

Source: Case study provided by the ACMHS

It was suggested that if outcome measurement is to become integral to advocacy practice, then appropriate outcome measures will need to be negotiated and an investment in the capacity to undertake data collection and analysis made by commissioners.

13

Optimum configuration and organisation of services

13.1 Characteristics of a quality advocacy service for African and Caribbean men

The following characteristics were identified as central to delivering high-quality advocacy for African and Caribbean men.

Being proactive
Advocacy services should be offered immediately on diagnosis or at first point of contact with other agencies such as the police or probation service.

Ensuring access
Steps need to be taken to ensure that those most in need, and potentially most isolated, have access to mental health advocacy. Access involves the sensitive location of advocacy services and better systems for promoting uptake. For example, outreach into in-patient wards, and secure units, ward-based surgeries or support groups.

A quality service
A quality service that is going to meet the needs of African and Caribbean men should:

- be built on an understanding of cultural values and beliefs reflected in the way the service is organised;
- whenever possible, be provided by an advocate of the same cultural background;
- respect the need for privacy and confidentiality by offering choice in terms of ethnicity and gender;

- provide a holistic approach to ensure that underlying social disadvantage and racism are addressed;
- promote movement from advocacy partner, to volunteer and possibly advocate;
- work in partnership with a range of other organisations to ensure that an individual's advocacy needs are most appropriately met;
- be provided by staff that are trained and well supported;
- provide training for mental health staff to tackle cultural insensitivity and racism;
- identify clear outcomes and monitor these both at an individual and collective level;
- have a robust system of management and accountability;
- empower individuals to have a stake in the running of their advocacy organisation, for example, user involvement on advisory committees or as trustees;
- be independent of statutory services;
- be properly funded.

13.2 Developing a whole system of advocacy provision

There was a consensus that advocacy services, of whatever form, had developed haphazardly and reactively, with many gaps in service provision. Relatively few respondents articulated clear views on how best to configure or organise advocacy services to best meet the needs of African and Caribbean men with mental health problems. There were, however, a number of observations on how to address specific current shortcomings.

Advocacy and specialist services for African and Caribbean men should not be seen in isolation from other services:

'Choice is key. A range of advocacy services which include specialised African Caribbean organisations would be ideal.'

Generic mental health advocacy organisations, BME and African and Caribbean advocacy services need to work closely together and be viewed as part of a whole system of advocacy provision. This would begin to address gaps in provision and avoid demands being made on services not set up to meet them. This includes our findings that some African and Caribbean and BME services attract a range of clientele beyond their target group, especially if alternatives are absent or perceived to be of poor quality.

The majority of respondents made a case for separate culturally sensitive advocacy provision in the context of unmet needs and negative experiences of mainstream mental health services. Sometimes this was expressed as a pragmatic solution to acute or seemingly intractable problems, rather than constituting an ideal in itself. There are options for achieving closer, more integrated working between generic mental health advocacy services, BME and African and Caribbean mental health advocacy services. These include joint working and formalised arrangements through protocols but the option most commonly suggested was for generic and BME mental health advocacy services to be housed under the same roof –'together but separate'. However, our findings in relation to partnership working at present indicate that this is an area requiring urgent development as generic mental health advocacy services are sometimes unaware of the role played by African and Caribbean and BME organisations in relation to advocacy.

The need for more Black staff in generic advocacy services was also identified and seen as absolutely essential if BME or African and Caribbean mental health advocacy services are not available.

There was consensus that advocacy needed to cover the whole range of NHS mental health services, including acute in-patient, community care and secure services, and other locations such as prisons and police custody. However, most advocacy organisations have a more limited range, and will focus on one or two sectors of service provision; or they will operate in an urban location or a rural area, but seldom bridge both. The majority are restricted to in-patient settings. There are some continuity issues for clients making transitions between different elements of a service, for example, in-patient to community.

Within this whole system there is a clear role for second-tier organisations, such as Action 4 Advocacy, which do not directly provide advocacy but exist to support and develop advocacy. Arguably, this second-tier work promotes good practice regarding advocacy in relation to BME communities, for example bilingual advocacy,[201] and could play a central role in future developments.

13.3 Funding insecurities: placing the results at risk

There is widespread concern about lack of funding and/or short-term funding. This is particularly evident for African and Caribbean organisations, with two well-respected African and Caribbean organisations losing funding for advocacy during the brief life of this review. The shift to commissioning from a grant-based system was perceived, at least in one instance, as adversely effecting the investment in community organisations and consequently appropriate advocacy.

For many service users the closure of valued services is viewed as politically motivated. Some continue to provide advocacy in the absence of dedicated funding. Further, many of the African and Caribbean mental health services are providing advocacy work but have never received funding to do so. Alternative services under the umbrella of statutory services are particularly vulnerable at times of budget pressure and cost cutting. On occasion, the funding situation was described as desperate.

The effect of service closures for advocacy partners should not be under-estimated. They frequently spoke about the sadness and distress associated with this. Raised expectations of appropriate and sensitive services would be dashed by their loss, engendering feelings of anger and pessimism for the future, and service users made it clear that they valued consistency, continuity and stability. There was also the possibility of organisational energy being diverted away from the core business, thus becoming focused on the survival of the organisation.

There was a sense that organisations did not have sufficient funding to do justice to their aims and objectives. The perception was that services had insufficient staff in relation to workload, making it difficult to contemplate improvements to services. Various groups reported doing more than they were paid or commissioned to do at present, working beyond their stated aims, boundaries, catchments or constituencies:

'Only a small charity, feel we probably do too much but don't have a system for limiting advocacy. Because ad hoc advocacy happens because service users choose to use us.'

Organisations were concerned about their ability to sustain themselves or cope with increasing demands, sustainability being defined as recognition for the quality of work undertaken as well as resources. The infrastructure within organisations could be vulnerable to funding pressures. This might involve lack of access to quality training opportunities for project staff and/or volunteers or not having an adequate budget to facilitate systems of staff supervision, especially external case supervision. Indeed some organisations declined to participate in our Practice Survey, indicating time would be better spent pursuing funding rather than supporting research.

13.4 Commissioning: planning and purchasing for advocacy

Interviews with commissioners elicited conflicting information regarding their preparedness and commitment to best meet the needs posed by African and Caribbean men for mental health advocacy. Specific issues arise across different UK national contexts, with particular concern about funding arrangements in Wales, where one BME organisation attempts to cover the whole country, and Northern Ireland, where no culturally specific advocacy provision was identified.

There was an apparent lack of specificity in some of the service-level agreements that have been developed. The fact that commissioning responsibilities were often shared between health and social services bodies added to the confusion. Commissioners such as primary care trusts (PCTs) reported activity to improve ethnicity monitoring and data collection, to eventually allow them to better assess community needs as a basis for appropriate services. At this time, however, data on the use of mental health services according to ethnicity is not routinely available across England, Wales and Northern Ireland. Nor do commissioners necessarily have a direct strategy in place for African and Caribbean men or a designated budget in this regard. There was awareness of relevant national initiatives, such as *Count me in*,[202] but the implications for the development and implementation of advocacy remain largely unexplored.

The broad range of social services responsibilities raises the question of competition for resources, between ethnic groups or with areas of need other than mental health. Further, the commissioning of advocacy services can be complicated by local service redesign. For example, in one area the reorganisation of mental health day services was impacting negatively on valued BVCS mental health services, resulting in closure.

Such initiatives may be justified by the rationale of mainstreaming services towards a general goal of promoting harmonious communities. However, a simple integrative approach does not take into account Black solidarity issues and historical notions of community-based BME services and mutual support – by definition these are segregated and building-based – offering immediate identity recognition and accessibility and outweighing concerns about stigma.

Some commissioners view the introduction of new community development workers (CDWs) as one way of addressing acknowledged failings in the delivery of effective services that are accessible to BME communities. However, concerns about demands being placed on CDWs and questions about their location, role and how they would work with African and Caribbean community and BME organisations were raised.

'… the PCT received the money for community development workers but they mismanage the money and wanted the advocacy service to take over the CDW role. The trust is under pressure to provide a CDW but is not providing it. We have also been asked to take on people from Eastern Europe and have said no because we feel we don't understand their issues or their culture.'

Relationships between commissioners and African and Caribbean communities in some areas were clearly under-developed. This was reflected in the comments by one commissioner about the ability of some BVCS organisations to be professional and accountable for their work. On the other hand, some BME mental health advocacy services were highly critical of commissioning bodies for an unsophisticated consideration of ethnicity issues.

It was observed that some organisations, especially smaller ones, could drift away from their original aims. There is clearly a need for formalised commissioning arrangements, such as contracts and service-level agreements, in ensuring fidelity to explicit aims and objectives. A further challenge for commissioning advocacy is the capacity within advocacy services to meet the potential demand if everyone was aware that they could have access to an advocate of their choice. Such concerns suggest the need for a national strategy to frame evaluation of advocacy needs, monitoring of patterns of service use and provision of high quality advocacy to support effective commissioning.

14

Transforming mental health services for African and Caribbean men

A significant theme deals with the need for wider reform or transformation of mental health services such that the needs of Black men are so much better served than at present. This was sometimes presented as an idealised or utopian alternative to the need for a separate African and Caribbean mental health advocacy.

> 'When people come across a project like [BME advocacy organisation] they see it as a saviour. A light at the end of the tunnel. In an ideal world I would like to see no need for this sort of project.'

These aspirations are typically accompanied by pessimism that they can be realised. More limited goals for wider mental health services include demands that the workforce more adequately represents the demographics of local communities:

> 'Need to change the profile of the workforce in the trust so that there are more BME staff to improve understanding and engagement with patients.'

This might extend to the NHS becoming better placed to meet culturally diverse needs, and minimise the recourse to damaging stereotypical representations of Black people, particularly the association of Black men with physicality, aggression and dangerousness.

The idealised hopes for equality of healthcare are set in juxtaposition to historical accounts of the emergence of BVCS organisations. Some advocacy organisations suggested that they 'only existed by default', meaning that they were there to meet the needs of Black people whose interests were not being served by mainstream health and social care providers. That is, they were not established by design of psychiatric or statutory services. The incidence of system failures involving Black patients, such as deaths while under care of mental health services, or failures of community care packages resulting in homicide or suicide in the community, has 'led to community groups to organise for themselves'.

Constructive suggestions for reform include how advocacy organisations could assist care provider organisations to make better assessments to identify core cultural needs, which clinical staff could then incorporate into more meaningful care planning and care programmes. Similarly, there could be contribution to staff training and consciousness-raising in relation to choice of treatments, negative experience of mental health services, racism and social disadvantage. There are demands for a more complete range of alternative therapies, and alternative conceptual frameworks for understanding the experiences and symptoms of service users.

Despite the growing rhetoric around recovery in modern mainstream mental health services, for service user participants in this study there was concern that such services do not assert recovery for African and Caribbean men. One service user observed 'they could be challenged and pushed further than they are, and this could be aided by specialist services'. Many service user participants spoke of the value of advocacy and specialist mental health services in language that was replete with notions of individual recovery and their own journey on it. The role of the advocate in all of this was often described as essential. Arguably, community-orientated Black specialist services have led the way in supporting a holistic view of recovery and the mainstream could learn from them. In this context, recovery was very much linked to community, re-integration into all aspects of one's community as an alternative to the isolation associated with mental ill health.

On a smaller scale of ambition, there were a number of calls for changes to some of the routine practices of mainstream mental health services to better facilitate the organisation and support of independent advocacy. These would include improvements to staff numbers, training and the quality of their relationships with service users – especially in terms of micro-level involvement in care planning and routine decision making, particularly concerning medication prescriptions. This should be in tandem with more thorough involvement of families and enhanced provision of information. Practical issues included the timing, location and format of meetings such as case reviews and care coordination meetings. Advocates often have their time wasted attending meetings invariably organised for the convenience of others, or waiting around for a slot in an otherwise very long meeting.

15

Summary and conclusions

15.1 Limitations of the Practice Survey

This survey set out to explore the experiences of African and Caribbean men in relation to advocacy and the organisation of current provision. Difficulties in identifying men who had experience of advocacy were encountered and therefore they formed a small part of the final sample of men who were interviewed or participated in the focus group.

Finally, this review raises questions about the relationship between advocacy provision and demographic issues. This was not addressed by this review and is an area where further work needs to be done.

15.2 Current professional consensus

While the potential of advocacy for African and Caribbean men is recognised, access is limited with scant evidence of developments in advocacy-focused organisations to engage with this client group. The mistrust of established mental health services and confusion over the meaning of advocacy also acts as a barrier to African and Caribbean men realising its value and potential benefits.

The development of mental health advocacy has been significant during the past 10 years and has largely focused on generic advocacy organisations. It has consisted of two main strands: first, attempts at producing standards, with the aim of strengthening the quality and accountability of current provision. Second, reviews of best practice towards a consensus of definition of advocacy, exemplified by the definiton of independent specialist mental health advocacy[203] with the emergence of professionalisation of advocacy. There has not been a consensus about the provision of mental health advocacy with BME communities, including African and Caribbean men, and as the research review found, relatively scant literature exists. This Practice Survey has established that there is agreement across different stakeholder groups that African and

Caribbean men require advocacy that is culturally sensitive, addresses their experiences of negative interactions with mental health services and facilitates recovery and social inclusion. Whether mental health advocacy should be provided by a generic BME or an African and Caribbean organisation predominantly reflected the ethnic affiliation of respondents but also demographic considerations.

Choice emerged as a central principle and the gender of the advocate also appears to be important. There was also agreement that it is essential that advocacy services are independent of statutory provision and some standards advocate complete independence from service provision. The co-existence of advocacy alongside other services in the BVCS may have arisen out of necessity but also reflects a different approach to advocacy.

15.3 Custom and practice

Building on the Research Review, available standards for advocacy practice conform to a notion of independent, professional advocacy or casework advocacy. At least in part, this is at odds with ways in which advocacy is organised in the BVCS. It is evident here that to some extent, where there is capacity and resources, such independent/professional/casework advocacy has been developed. Yet, in the majority there has been the development of alternative models, as part of a wider more holistic approach. This is often geared towards collective goals such as addressing inequalities and realising an individual's potential in the round.

15.4 Emerging new practice

Delivering race equality in mental health care,[204] and the previous publications that led up to its development,[205] signal a different approach to providing services to BME communities. Central to this is the concept of community engagement, giving community organisation the resources and authority to define their own needs. This sits comfortably with definitions of advocacy. However, this is happening at the same time as well-respected BVCS organisations face acute financial pressures, insecurity of future funding and possible closure.

CDWs are a new role, encompassing a number of dimensions that are being brought in under the aegis of the national DRE agenda. It is evident that there are a number of areas of overlap between the expectations of these roles and the work carried out by BVCS organisations covered in this Practice Survey. As the role is new, some commissioners appear uncertain of the role and the most appropriate location for these workers. The impact of the DRE programme has been called into question by some commentators, inclusive of a critique that the targets for implementation of CDWs have not been met. This has led to calls for the redirection of the available resources into strengthening the existing BVCS.[206]

The development of the independent mental capacity advocate (IMCA) is clearly resonant with the aforementioned trend towards professionalisation and standardisation. Towards the end of the time period covered by this Practice Survey a number of tenders have been advertised for the establishment of IMCAs. On the face of it, there is a real risk that this form of advocacy is developing in a way that further neglects specialist needs relating to ethnicity and culture.

Although not a direct part of this survey, there is evidence of good practice emerging in terms of bilingual advocacy in support of refugees and asylum seekers; again, the extent to which this can develop is significantly hindered by low levels of funding.

16

Synthesis

16.1 Needs and experiences of African and Caribbean men

All sources expressed concerns about unmet need and the negative experiences of mainstream mental health provision by African and Caribbean men. The research literature is consistent and points to a negative relationship between mental health services and African and Caribbean men resulting in a lack of inclination to seek help or comply with treatment, leading to relapse and readmission. The evidence from the African and Caribbean men, the organisations supporting them and from descriptions of advocacy services for African and Caribbean communities support this and highlight the racism and discrimination that they encounter in their experience of mental health services. The men also highlighted concerns and needs about daily living and concrete practical support that they thought would be helpful to them.

16.2 Provision of advocacy

The need for advocacy to address these issues is identified by key reports, including government policy. However, the lack of appropriate provision is highlighted both within the Research Review and the Practice Survey, with strong evidence that mental health advocacy services in general do not engage with African and Caribbean men. In part, this reflects the widespread absence of a strategic approach to the development of mental health advocacy with a lack of vision of how mental health advocacy can be developed to meet the diverse range of needs of all those with mental health problems.

Mental health advocacy with African and Caribbean men can potentially be provided by a range of organisations but in practice is mainly provided by BVCS. The evidence for the impact of advocacy on any of the outcome areas identified was weak. Across the different organisations empowerment, albeit loosely defined, and the goal of self-advocacy were identified as key outcomes. Having a greater say and greater control, particularly in the relationship with mental health services and therefore the capacity to determine what treatment and support you received, were therefore viewed as critical elements of advocacy. However, BVCS organisations providing advocacy went further and identified this as only one aspect of the work that they were engaged in, which aimed to try and meet a broad range of social needs. This reflects a concern to tackle social disadvantage and the roots of this disadvantage, including racism, and therefore the outcomes are framed in broader terms – getting a job, starting a course and improving relationships with family members for instance.

There was a broad consensus that advocacy services have to be culturally sensitive and all primary studies pointed to the importance of this. However, the articulation of what this meant by generic mental health advocacy services, and the material relating to these was under-developed. This suggests either a lack of understanding of what this means or how to achieve it, or that it is a low priority. There is material both in relation to generic health advocacy and mental health advocacy for people from BME communities, and these sources highlight the difficulty that exists in terms of framing advocacy in a way that is relevant to BME communities and securing adequate and sustainable investment to meet the advocacy needs of these communities.

The need for advocates to have a shared cultural heritage (that is, 'an advocate like me') was emphasised by African and Caribbean services users, organisation supporting them and the literature on service development for these communities. Trust is an important dimension of this and was recognised widely by these sources as facilitating access and engagement with advocacy services. The advocates' and organisations' roots in the community and the understanding of discrimination, racism and Black history as well as Black identity served to build confidence in the ability of the service to accurately listen, understand and act on the service user's behalf. The extent to which this needed to be an African and Caribbean organisation as opposed to a more broadly constituted BME organisation was unclear and the position on this appeared to reflect the ethnic affiliation of the source of the evidence. On the one hand, there was a consensus among generic mainstream advocacy services, and the studies of mental health advocacy, that there should be specific provision for BME communities, inclusive of African and Caribbean communities. On the other hand, the majority of African and Caribbean service users and African and Caribbean organisations identified the importance of shared African and Caribbean heritage as an important characteristic both of the advocate and of the service.

The review differentiates between two levels of mechanisms for advocacy. First, what sort of advocacy works for whom under what circumstances? This review has generated hypotheses about how advocacy could work to enable African and Caribbean men to access more appropriate mental health services. The capacity of the organisation and advocates to engage with people early on, in non-threatening ways and to provide continuity emerge as important. Second, barriers and facilitators to the provision of advocacy have been identified and there was a consensus across the different forms of evidence that stability of funding is critical. While an issue for advocacy services in general, African and Caribbean organisations appeared to be particularly vulnerable with a number of such organisations losing their funding during the course of the review, including one of our partner organisations.

16.3 Organisational arrangements

In answering the review question, there are structural and operational issues to consider. The review has identified features of good practice. In terms of organisational arrangements to support the delivery of this positive practice, we found that there is in general a trade-off between cultural sensitivity and capacity to deliver advocacy. There are potentially a number of ways of resolving this to improve advocacy provision to African and Caribbean men. The possible options are not mutually exclusive and are as follows:

1. Increased investment in the BVCS to develop and strengthen mental health advocacy either as part of an African and Caribbean or a BME-focused mental health service. This has been called for by other studies concerned with mental health activity provided by the BVCS (see, for example, Christie and Hill[207]; Chouhan and MacAttram[208]).
2. Investment in the development of organisations that do not directly provide advocacy but aim to build capacity in the development of advocacy (that is, second-tier organisations) for African and Caribbean

communities in BVCS and the mainstream advocacy sector. The need for this type of investment in strengthening the capacity of the BVCS has also been highlighted by the authors cited above.

3. Develop African and Caribbean mental health advocacy under the umbrella of generic mental health advocacy provision.

4. Develop advocacy as a whole system with different forms of advocacy – professional casework advocacy, culturally specific advocacy, community advocacy etc – available with coordination and sufficient integration to facilitate cross-referrals and improve access. This means more than the co-existence of different forms of advocacy as is currently found in some places. For a whole system to work there needs to be good coordination and clear routes through from one service to another so that the service user is not left to navigate a bewildering array of options. Co-location of services would clearly facilitate this.

There are a number of points to make in relation to these options. First, the development of mental health advocacy needs to be considered for both men and women in the African and Caribbean community and whether particular needs are better served by advocacy that is gender-specific. Service users did express a preference for choice of gender but there was no evidence to evaluate whether gender-specific provision is better. It was evident that attention needed to be paid to the advocacy needs of African and Caribbean women and it was clear that they too are over-represented in admissions and detention to psychiatric care.[209]

Second, the needs within African and Caribbean communities are different – these communities are heterogeneous. An obvious difference is between established communities and refugees and asylum seekers who are newly arrived. Mental health need among asylum seekers and refugees is high and it is suggested that they require dedicated advocacy provision.[210]

17

Conclusion

The context for advocacy provision is changing with an increased policy emphasis on choice, independence and service user-led commissioning in the form of Direct Payments and individualised budgets. It is clear that if African and Caribbean (and indeed other BME communities) are not to be left behind, that a more thoughtful approach to the development of mental health advocacy is required. It requires that commissioners and providers understand the issues faced by African and Caribbean men, how advocacy might help and what outcomes it could deliver. This process necessarily requires engagement with African and Caribbean communities and the model for community engagement developed by the Centre for Ethnicity and Health at the University of Central Lancashire (UCLAN) provides a method for this.[211] Methods were also developed during the course of the review and in particular engaging with men on their terms about the issues that were important to them emerged as an important first principle. The process also requires transparency and clarity about decision making.

This review has not identified a single preferred organisational model for the development of mental health advocacy for African and Caribbean men. It has, however identified potential options for commissioners and their partners to consider.

In arriving at a decision commissioners will need to map provision to need and available resources. In doing so they will need to take into account not only the demographic profile but also the over-representation of African and Caribbean men and women, and indeed under-representation of other groups, within mental health services. The engagement of communities in this process is essential.

It will be evident from this process, as indeed it was evident from the review, that the capacity of the BVCS needs strengthening to deliver mental health advocacy and that there needs to be the development of second-tier organisations. Partnership and the development of a whole system of advocacy provision, although a relatively minor theme to emerge from the Research Review and the Practice Survey, requires attention. It is evident that the organic development of advocacy within BVCS has preserved a holistic and collective model of advocacy. It is important that this model is not disadvantaged or dismissed in any future moves to formalise advocacy and the development of more systematic commissioning arrangements.

The development of a whole system of advocacy could serve to benefit all members of the community, including BME communities. While enabling diverse needs to be met it could also enable joint initiatives, training and capacity building to take place. Further, the exposure to other models of advocacy for other care groups, and in particular the developments in learning disability advocacy, could broaden the approach to mental health advocacy.

The developments in commissioning with the publication of a joint commissioning framework, the duty for integrated needs assessment, the focus on outcome-led commissioning and the opportunities in relation to social enterprises are all opportunities that could support developments in advocacy for all BME communities, including African and Caribbean men. For this to happen there needs to be positive leadership at a national and local level. The CDWs may be ideally placed to take forward this agenda at a local level in partnership with BME communities and local commissioners. DRE identifies culturally appropriate advocacy as an area of action key for PCTs and it is now imperative that action is taken to deliver this.

To conclude, it is clear that there is a consensus that African and Caribbean men require advocacy that addresses their experiences of negative interactions with mental health services and facilitates recovery and social inclusion. The typically holistic, collective and transformative philosophy of BVCS means that advocacy rooted within these organisations is potentially aligned with current models of recovery. Thus advocacy with African and Caribbean men has the potential to not only ensure the delivery of more appropriate and effective mainstream services and facilitate individual empowerment but also to contribute to addressing underling social disadvantage, social exclusion and inequalities.

References

1   Mind (2006) *With us in mind: Service user recommendations for advocacy standards in England*, London: Mind.

2   Baptiste, M. (2003) 'African mental health', *Diverse Minds Magazine*, 15-16 November.

3   Winterton, R. (2006) 'Black and minority ethnic mental health', Letter to SHA chief executives, 4 October, Department of Health.

4   Bhugra, D. and Bahl, V. (1999) *Ethnicity: An agenda for mental health*, London: Gaskell.

5   McClean, C., Campbell, C. and Cornish, F. (2002) 'African-Caribbean interactions with mental health services in the UK: experiences and expectations of exclusion as (re)productive of health inequalities', *Social Science & Medicine*, vol 56, no 3, pp 657-69.

6   Healthcare Commission, Mental Health Act Commission and National Institute for Mental Health in England (2005) *Count me in: Results of a national census of inpatients in mental health hospitals and facilities in England and Wales*, London: Healthcare Commission.

7   Bhui, K., Christie, Y. and Bhugra, D. (1995) 'The essential elements of culturally sensitive psychiatric services', *International Journal of Social Psychiatry*, vol 41, no 4, pp 242-56.

8   McClean, C., Campbell, C. and Cornish, F. (2002) 'African-Caribbean interactions with mental health services in the UK: experiences and expectations of exclusion as (re)productive of health inequalities', *Social Science & Medicine*, vol 56, no 3, pp 657-69.

9   Keating, F., Robertson, D., McCulloch, A. and Francis, E. (2002) *Breaking the circles of fear: A review of the relationship between mental health services and African and Caribbean communities*, London: SCMH.

10 Healthcare Commission, Mental Health Act Commission and National Institute for Mental Health in England (2005) *Count me in: Results of a national census of inpatients in mental health hospitals and facilities in England and Wales*, London: Healthcare Commission.

11   Healthcare Commission, Care Services Improvement Partnership and National Institute for Mental Health in England (2007) *Count me in: Results of the 2006 national census of inpatients in mental health and learning disability services in England and Wales*, London: Healthcare Commission.

12   Blofeld, J. (2003) *Independent inquiry into the death of David Bennett*, Norwich: Norfolk, Suffolk and Cambridge Strategic Health Authority.

13   Ludwig, A. (2001) 'Access to advocacy', *Diverse Minds Magazine*, Issue 10, October, pp 12-13.

14   Barnes, D. and Tate, A. (2000) *Advocacy from the outside inside: A review of the patients' advocacy service at Ashworth Hospital*, Durham: University of Durham/Ashworth Hospital Authority/North West Region NHS Secure Commissioning Team.

15   Bowes, A.M., Valenti, M., Sim, D. and Macintosh, S. (2002) *Delivering advocacy services to Glasgow's Black and minority ethnic communities: Report to Glasgow City Council and Greater Glasgow Health Board*, Stirling: Department of Applied Social Science, University of Stirling, Greater Glasgow Health Board.
See also: Cambridge, P. and Wiliams, L. (2004) 'Approaches to advocacy for refugees and asylum seekers: a development case study for local support and advice service', *Journal of Refugees Studies*, vol 17, no 1, pp 97-113.

16   Bhui, K., Christie, Y. and Bhugra, D. (1995) 'The essential elements of culturally sensitive psychiatric services', *International Journal of Social Psychiatry*, vol 41, no 4, pp 242-56.

17   Healthcare Commission, Mental Health Act Commission and National Institute for Mental Health in England (2005) *Count me in: Results of a national census of inpatients in mental health hospitals and facilities in England and Wales*, London: Healthcare Commission.

18   Healthcare Commission, Mental Health Act Commission and National Institute for Mental Health in England (2007) *Count me in: Results of the 2006 national census of inpatients in mental health in mental health and learning disability services in England and Wales*, London: Healthcare Commission.

19 Bhui, K.,Stansfeld, S.A., Holt, S., Priebe, S., Mole, F. and Feder, G. (2003) 'Ethnic variations in the pathways to and use of specialist mental health services', *British Journal of Psychiatry*, vol 182, pp 105-16.

20 Browne, D. (1997) *Black people and sectioning. The Black experience of detention under the Civil Sections of the Mental Health Act*, London: Little Rock Publishing.

21 Morgan, C., Mallett, R., Hutchinson, G., Bagalkote, K., Morgan, K., Fearon, P., Dazzan, J., Boydell, K., McKenzie, G., Harrison, G., Murray, R., Jones, P., Craig, T., Leff, J. and on behalf of the Aesop Study Group (2005) 'Pathways to care and ethnicity. 1: Sample characteristics and compulsory admission, Report from the Aesop Study', *British Journal of Psychiatry*, vol 186, no 4, April, pp 281-9.

22 Sainsbury Centre for Mental Health (2006) *The costs of race inequality*, London: SCMH.

23 Healthcare Commission, Mental Health Act Commission and National Institute for Mental Health in England (2005) *Count me in: Results of a national census of inpatients in mental health hospitals and facilities in England and Wales*, London: Healthcare Commission.

24 Morgan, C., Mallett, R., Hutchinson, G. and Leff, J. (2004) 'Negative pathways to psychiatric care and ethnicity: the bridge between social science and psychiatry', *Social Science & Medicine*, vol 58, no 4, pp 739-52.

25 Hutchinson, G. and Gilvarry, C. (1998) 'Ethnicity and dissatisfaction with mental health services', *British Journal of Psychiatry*, vol 172, pp 95-6.

26 Burnett, R., Mallett, R., Bhugra, D., Der, G., Hutchinson, G.G. and Leff, J. (1999) 'The first contact of patients with schizophrenia with psychiatric services: social pathways to care in a multi-ethnic population', *Psychological Medicine*, vol 29, no 2, pp 475-83.

27 Sharpley, M., Hutchinson, G., McKenzie, K. and Murray, R.M. (2001) 'Understanding the excess of psychosis among the African-Caribbean population in England. Review of current hypotheses', *British Journal of Psychiatry – Supplementum*, vol 40, s 60-8.

28 Keating, F., Robertson, D., McCulloch, A. and Francis, E. (2002) *Breaking the circles of fear: A review of the relationship between mental health services and African and Caribbean communities*, London: SCMH.

29 McClean, C., Campbell, C. and Cornish, F. (2002) 'African-Caribbean interactions with mental health services in the UK: experiences and expectations of exclusion as (re)productive of health inequalities', *Social Science & Medicine*, vol 56, no 3, pp 657-69.

30 Sainsbury Centre for Mental Health (2006) *The costs of race inequality*, London: SCMH.

31 Adams, P., Llitchmore-Grant, J., McKoy, G., Gonzales, A., Willimas, G. and Markland, L. (2006) 'Report of the community led research project focusing on the role faith communities can play in the mental health service needs of the African and Caribbean community in Luton', UCLAN, unpublished report.

32 Keating, F., Robertson, D., McCulloch, A. and Francis, E. (2002) *Breaking the circles of fear: A review of the relationship between mental health services and African and Caribbean communities*, London: SCMH.

33 Department of Health (1999) *National Service Framework for mental health*, London: The Stationery Office.

34 National Institute for Mental Health in England (2003) *Inside outside: Improving mental health services for Black and minority ethnic communities in England*, London: DH.

35 Blofeld, J. (2003) *Independent inquiry into the death of David Bennett*, Norwich: Norfolk, Suffolk and Cambridge Strategic Health Authority.

36 Macpherson, W. (1999) *The Stephen Lawrence Inquiry*, London: The Stationery Office.

37 Department of Health (2005) *Delivering race equality in mental health care and the government's response to the independent inquiry into the death of David Bennett*, London: DH.

38 Department of Health (2005) *Community development workers for Black and minority ethnic communities: Education and training – Supplementary guidance* (www.dh.gov.uk/en/Publicationsandstatistics/Publications/PublicationsPolicyAndGuidance/DH_4120648).

39 Welsh Assembly Government (2006) *Raising the standard: Race equality action plan for adult mental health services in Wales* (http://new.wales.gov.uk/topics/health/nhswales/healthservice/ mental_health_services/raceequalityactionplan?lang=en).

40 Welsh Assembly Government (2006) *Raising the standard: The revised adult mental health National Service Framework and an action plan for Wales*, Cardiff: Welsh Assembly (www.wales.nhs. uk/documents/raceequalityEBOOK-15-11-6.pdf).

41 Department of Health, Social Services and Public Safety (2006) *Human rights and equal opportunity: The Bamford review of mental health and learning disability (Northern Ireland)*, Northern Ireland: Department of Health, Social Services and Public Safety.

42 Department of Health (2004) *Draft Mental Health Bill*, London: The Stationery Office.

42a Mental Health Bill (2006): Amendments to Mental health Act 1983 (www.publications.parliament.uk/pa/cm200607/ cmbills/107/2007107.pdf).

43 Mental Capacity Act (2005) London: The Stationery Office.

44 Department of Health (2006) *Our health, our care, our say*, London: DH.

45 Disability Rights Commission (2006) *Delivering the choice and voice agenda: The role of independent advocacy services*, DRC.

46 Scottish Executive (2001) *Independent advocacy: A guide for commissioners*, Edinburgh: Scottish Executive.

47 Silvera, M. and Kapasi, R. (2004) *Health advocacy for minority ethnic Londoners: Putting services on the map*, London: King's Fund.

48 Silvera, M. and Kapasi, R. (2004) *Health advocacy for minority ethnic Londoners: Putting services on the map*, London: King's Fund.

49 Heer, B. (2004) *Building bridges for health: Exploring the potential for advocacy in London*, London: King's Fund.

50 Atkinson, D. (2000) *Advocacy: A review*, York: Joseph Rowntree Foundation.

51 Mellanby, K. (2004) 'Charter impact', *Planet Advocacy*, June, p 6.

52 Action 4 Advocacy (2002) *The advocacy charter*, London: Action 4 Advocacy.

53 World Health Organisation (2003) *Advocacy for mental health*, Geneva: WHO (www.who.int/mental_health/resources/en/Advocacy.pdf).

54 World Health Organisation (2004) *Empowerment and mental health advocacy*, WHO European Ministerial Conference on Mental Health Briefing, Geneva: WHO.

55 World Health Organisation (2003) *Advocacy for mental health*, Geneva: WHO (www.who.int/mental_health/resources/en/Advocacy.pdf).

56 Rai-Atkins, A., Jama, A.A., Wright, N., Scott, V., Perring, C., Craig, G. and Katbamna, S. (2002) *Best practice in mental health: Advocacy for African, Caribbean and South Asian communities*, Bristol: The Policy Press.

57 Rai-Atkins, A., Jama, A.A., Wright, N., Scott, V., Perring, C., Craig, G. and Katbamna, S. (2002) *Best practice in mental health: Advocacy for African, Caribbean and South Asian communities*, Bristol: The Policy Press.

58 Rai-Atkins, A., Jama, A.A., Wright, N., Scott, V., Perring, C., Craig, G. and Katbamna, S. (2002) *Best practice in mental health: Advocacy for African, Caribbean and South Asian communities*, Bristol: The Policy Press.

59 Carlisle, S. (2000) 'Health promotion, advocacy and health inequalities: a conceptual framework', *Health Promotion International*, vol 35, no 4, pp 369-76.

60 Henderson, R. and Pochin, M. (2001) *A right result? Advocacy, justice and empowerment*, Bristol: The Policy Press.

61 Rai-Atkins, A., Jama, A.A., Wright, N., Scott, V., Perring, C., Craig, G. and Katbamna, S. (2002) *Best practice in mental health: Advocacy for African, Caribbean and South Asian communities*, Bristol: The Policy Press.

62 Pawson, R., Boaz, A., Grayson, L., Long, A. and Barnes, C. (2003) *Types and quality of knowledge in social care*, Knowledge Review 3, London: SCIE.

63 Long, A.F., Grayson, L. and Boaz, A. (2006) 'Assessing the quality of knowledge in social care: exploring the potential of a set of generic standards', *British Journal of Social Work*, vol 36, no 2, pp 207-26.

64 Pawson, R., Boaz, A., Grayson, L., Long, A. and Barnes, C. (2003) *Types and quality of knowledge in social care*, Knowledge Review 3, London: SCIE.

65 Agree Collaboration (2001) *Appraisal of guidelines for research and evaluation* (www.agreecollaboration.org).

66 Bowes, A.M., Valenti, M., Sim, D. and Macintosh, S. (2002) *Delivering advocacy services to Glasgow's Black and minority ethnic communities: Report to Glasgow City Council and Greater Glasgow Health Board*, Stirling: Department of Applied Social Science, University of Stirling.

67 Keating, F., Robertson, D., McCulloch, A. and Francis, E. (2002) *Breaking the circles of fear: A review of the relationship between mental health services and African and Caribbean communities*, London: SCMH.

68 Turner, M. (2003) *Shaping our lives: From outset to outcome; what people think of the social care services they use*, York: Joseph Rowntree Foundation.

69 The Civis Trust (2005) *Early intervention in the mental health needs of Asian and African-Caribbean communities*, London: Civis Consultants.

70 Stein, D.J., Wessels, C., Zungu-Dirwayi, N., Berk, M. and Wilson, Z. (2001) 'Value and effectiveness of consumer advocacy groups: a survey of the anxiety disorders support group in South Africa', *Depression & Anxiety*, vol 13, no 2, pp 105-7.

71 Weisman, R.L., Lamberti, J.S. and Price, N. (2004) 'Integrating criminal justice, community healthcare, and support services for adults with severe mental disorders', *Psychiatric Quarterly*, vol 75, no 1, pp 71-85.

72 Heer, B. (2004) *Building bridges for health: Exploring the potential of advocacy in London*, London: King's Fund.

73 Carlisle, S. (2000) 'Health promotion, advocacy and health inequalities: a conceptual framework', *Health Promotion International*, vol 35, no 4, pp 369-76.

74 Rai-Atkins, A., Jama, A.A., Wright, N., Scott, V., Perring, C., Craig, G. and Katbamna, S. (2002) *Best practice in mental health: Advocacy for African, Caribbean and South Asian communities*, Bristol: The Policy Press.

75 Silvera, M. and Kapasi, R. (2004) *Health advocacy for minority ethnic Londoners: Putting services on the map*, London: King's Fund.

76 Bowes, A.M., Valenti, M., Sim, D. and Macintosh, S. (2002) *Delivering advocacy services to Glasgow's Black and minority ethnic communities: Report to Glasgow City Council and Greater Glasgow Health Board*, Glasgow: Department of Applied Social Science, University of Stirling and Greater Glasgow Health Board.

77 Rai-Atkins, A., Jama, A.A., Wright, N., Scott, V., Perring, C., Craig, G. and Katbamna, S. (2002) *Best practice in mental health: Advocacy for African, Caribbean and South Asian communities*, Bristol: The Policy Press.

78 Chouhan, K. and MacAttram, M. (2005) *Towards a blueprint for action: Building capacity in the black and minority ethnic voluntary and community sector providing mental health services*, London: Greater London Authority.

79 Kapasi, R. and Silvera, M. (2002) *A standards framework for delivering effective health and social care advocacy for Black and minority ethnic Londoners*, London: Silkap Consultants for King's Fund.

80 Rai-Atkins, A., Jama, A.A., Wright, N., Scott, V., Perring, C., Craig, G. and Katbamna, S. (2002) *Best practice in mental health: Advocacy for African, Caribbean and South Asian communities*, Bristol: The Policy Press.

81 Advocacy 2000 (2002) *Principles and standards in independent advocacy organsiations and groups*, Edinburgh: Advocacy 2000.

82 Mind (2006) *With us in mind: Service user recommendations for advocacy standards in England*, London: Mind.

83 Brent Advocacy Concerns (2005) *Standards manual* (draft edition), London: BAC.

84 Barnes, D., Brandon, T. and Webb, T. (2002) *Independent specialist advocacy in England and Wales: Recommendations for good practice*, Durham: University of Durham.

85 Mullins, G. and Wood, P. (2004) *A clear voice, a clear vision: The advocacy reader*, Sheffield: UKAN.

86 Mind (2006) *With us in mind: Service user recommendations for advocacy standards in England*, London: Mind.

87 Action 4 Advocacy (2006) *Quality standards for advocacy schemes*, London: Action 4 Advocacy.

88 Brent Advocacy Concerns (2005) *Standards manual* (draft edition), London: BAC.

89 Leeds Advocacy Network (2005) *Leeds advocacy standards* (www. advocacy-network-leeds.org.uk/standard/gpgwelc1.html).

90 Chouhan, K. and MacAttram, M. (2005) *Towards a blueprint for action: Building capacity in the Black and minority ethnic voluntary and community sector providing mental health services*, London: Greater London Authority.

91 Wood, P. and UK Advocacy Network (2004) *Advocacy standards: Standards for advocacy in mental health*, Sheffield: UK Advocacy Network.

92 Advocacy 2000 (2002) *Principles and standards in independent advocacy organsiations and groups*, Edinburgh: Advocacy 2000.

93 Kapasi, R. and Silvera, M. (2002) *A standards framework for delivering effective health and social care advocacy for Black and minority ethnic Londoners*, London: Silkap Consultants for King's Fund.

94 Rai-Atkins, A., Jama, A.A., Wright, N., Scott, V., Perring, C., Craig, G. and Katbamna, S. (2002) *Best practice in mental health: Advocacy for African, Caribbean and South Asian communities*, Bristol: The Policy Press.

95 Barnes, D., Brandon, T. and Webb, T. (2002) *Independent specialist advocacy in England and Wales: Recommendations for good practice*, Durham: University of Durham.

96 Mullins, G. and Wood, P. (2004) *A clear voice, a clear vision: The advocacy reader*, Sheffield: UKAN.

97 Scottish Executive (2001) *Independent advocacy: A guide for commissioners*, Edinburgh: Scottish Executive.

98 UK Advocacy Network (1994) *Advocacy: A code of practice*, Sheffield: UKAN.

99 Read, J. and Wallcraft, J. (1994) *Guidelines on advocacy for mental health workers*, London: Mind and UNISON.

100 Mellanby, K. (2002) *Advocacy training in London: Exploring opportunities and need*, London: Advocacy Across London.

101 Huijbers, K. (2005) *Learning for the sector in action for advocacy: Annual review 2004-2005* (www.actionforadvocacy.org.uk).

102 Christie, Y. and Hill, N. (2003) *Black Spaces Project*, London: Mental Health Foundation.
Also Hill, N. (2003) 'Safe passage', *Community Care*, 3 October.

103 Mind (2006) *With us in mind: Service user recommendations for advocacy standards in England*, London: Mind.

104 Coleman, C. and Dunmur, J. (2000) *Surveying mental health advocacy needs in Sheffield*, Sheffield: Sheffield Community Health Council.

105 Platzer, H. and Foley, R. (2004) *Mental health advocacy in London: A mapping report*, London: London Development Centre.

106 Chouhan, K. and MacAttram, M. (2005) *Towards a blueprint for action: Building capacity in the black and minority ethnic voluntary and community sector providing mental health services*, London: Greater London Authority.

107 Christie, Y. and Hill, N. (2003) *Black Spaces Project*, London: Mental Health Foundation.

108 Rai-Atkins, A., Jama, A.A., Wright, N., Scott, V., Perring, C., Craig, G. and Katbamna, S. (2002) *Best practice in mental health: Advocacy for African, Caribbean and South Asian communities*, Bristol: The Policy Press.

109 Mind (2006) *With us in mind: Service user recommendations for advocacy standards in England*, London: Mind.

110 McKeown, M., Bingley, W. and Denoual, I. (2002) *A review of mental health advocacy services at the Edenfield Regional Secure Unit and Bowness High Dependency Unit, Prestwich Hospital*, Preston: UCLAN/North West Secure Commissioning Team.

111 Barnes, D. and Tate, A. (2000) *Advocacy from the outside inside: A review of the patients' advocacy service at Ashworth Hospital*, Durham: University of Durham/Ashworth Hospital Authority/North West Region NHS Secure Commissioning Team.

112 Chouhan, K. and MacAttram, M. (2005) *Towards a blueprint for action: Building capacity in the black and minority ethnic voluntary and community sector providing mental health services*, London: Greater London Authority.

113 Also Hill, N. (2003) 'Safe passage', *Community Care*, 3 October.

114 Watters, C. (1996) 'Inequalities in mental health: the inner city mental health project', *Journal of Community & Applied Social Psychology*, vol 6, pp 383-394.

115 Also Platzer, H. and Foley, R. (2004) *Mental health advocacy in London: A mapping report*, London: London Development Centre.
Also see Foley, H. and Platzer, R. (2006) 'Place and provision: mapping mental health advocacy services in London', *Social Science & Medicine*, vol 64, no 3, pp 617-632.

116 Mind (2006) *With us in mind: Service user recommendations for advocacy standards in England*, London: Mind.

117 Rai-Atkins, A., Jama, A.A., Wright, N., Scott, V., Perring, C., Craig, G. and Katbamna, S. (2002) *Best practice in mental health: Advocacy for African, Caribbean and South Asian communities*, Bristol: The Policy Press.

118 McKeown, M., Bingley, W. and Denoual, I. (2002) *A review of mental health advocacy services at the Edenfield Regional Secure Unit and Bowness High Dependency Unit, Prestwich Hospital*, Preston: UCLAN/North West Secure Commissioning Team.

119 Coleman, C. and Dunmur, J. (2000) *Surveying mental health advocacy needs in Sheffield*, Sheffield: Sheffield Community Health Council.

120 Barnes, D. and Tate, A. (2000) *Advocacy from the outside inside: A review of the patients' advocacy service at Ashworth Hospital*, University of Durham/Ashworth Hospital Authority/North West Region NHS Secure Commissioning Team.

121 Rai-Atkins, A., Jama, A.A., Wright, N., Scott, V., Perring, C., Craig, G. and Katbamna, S. (2002) *Best practice in mental health: Advocacy for African, Caribbean and South Asian communities*, Bristol: The Policy Press.

122 Foley, H. and Platzer, R. (2006) 'Place and provision: mapping mental health advocacy services in London', *Social Science & Medicine*, vol 64, no 3, pp 617-632.

123 Platzer, H. and Foley, R. (2004) *Mental health advocacy in London: A mapping report*, London: London Development Centre.

124 Chouhan, K. and MacAttram, M. (2005) *Towards a blueprint for action: Building capacity in the black and minority ethnic voluntary and community sector providing mental health services*, London: Greater London Authority.

125 Christie, Y. and Hill, N. (2003) *Black Spaces Project*, London: Mental Health Foundation.

126 Watters, C. (1996) 'Inequalities in mental health: the inner city mental health project', *Journal of Community & Applied Social Psychology*, vol 6, pp 383-394.

127 Rai-Atkins, A., Jama, A.A., Wright, N., Scott, V., Perring, C., Craig, G. and Katbamna, S. (2002) *Best practice in mental health: Advocacy for African, Caribbean and South Asian communities*, Bristol: The Policy Press.

128 Platzer, H. and Foley, R. (2004) *Mental health advocacy in London: A mapping report*, London: London Development Centre.

129 Foley, R. and Platzer, H. (2002) 'A good place to talk: mapping mental health advocacy services in London using GIS', *Geo Health 2002*.

130 Mind (2006) *With us in mind: Service user recommendations for advocacy standards in England*, London: Mind.

131 McKeown, M., Bingley, W. and Denoual, I. (2002) *A review of mental health advocacy services at the Edenfield Regional Secure Unit and Bowness High Dependency Unit, Prestwich Hospital*, Preston: UCLAN/North West Secure Commissioning Team.

132 Coleman, C. and Dunmur, J. (2000) *Surveying mental health advocacy needs in Sheffield*, Sheffield: Sheffield Community Health Council.

133 Barnes, D. and Tate, A. (2000) *Advocacy from the outside inside: A review of the patients' advocacy service at Ashworth Hospital*, University of Durham/Ashworth Hospital Authority/North West Region NHS Secure Commissioning Team.

134 Rai-Atkins, A., Jama, A.A., Wright, N., Scott, V., Perring, C., Craig, G. and Katbamna, S. (2002) *Best practice in mental health: Advocacy for African, Caribbean and South Asian communities*, Bristol: The Policy Press.

135 Platzer, H. and Foley, R. (2004) *Mental health advocacy in London: A mapping report*, London: London Development Centre.

136 Rai-Atkins, A., Jama, A.A., Wright, N., Scott, V., Perring, C., Craig, G. and Katbamna, S. (2002) *Best practice in mental health: Advocacy for African, Caribbean and South Asian communities*, Bristol: The Policy Press.

137 Platzer, H. and Foley, R. (2004) *Mental health advocacy in London: A mapping report*, London: London Development Centre.

138 McKeown, M., Bingley, W. and Denoual, I. (2002) *A review of mental health advocacy services at the Edenfield Regional Secure Unit and Bowness High Dependency Unit, Prestwich Hospital*, Preston: UCLAN/North West Secure Commissioning Team.

139 Barnes, D. and Tate, A. (2000) *Advocacy from the outside inside: A review of the patients' advocacy service at Ashworth Hospital*, University of Durham/Ashworth Hospital Authority/North West Region NHS Secure Commissioning Team.

140 Chouhan, K. and MacAttram, M. (2005) *Towards a blueprint for action: Building capacity in the black and minority ethnic voluntary and community sector providing mental health services*, London: Greater London Authority.

141 Christie, Y. and Hill, N. (2003) *Black Spaces Project*, London: Mental Health Foundation.

142 Watters, C. (1996) 'Inequalities in mental health: the inner city mental health project', *Journal of Community: Applied Social Psychology*, vol 6, pp 383-394.

143 Chouhan, K. and MacAttram, M. (2005) *Towards a blueprint for action: Building capacity in the black and minority ethnic voluntary and community sector providing mental health services*, London: Greater London Authority.

144 Platzer, H. and Foley, R. (2004) *Mental health advocacy in London: A mapping report*, London: London Development Centre.

145 Watters, C. (1996) 'Inequalities in mental health: the inner city mental health project', *Journal of Community & Applied Social Psychology*, vol 6, pp 383-394.

146 Sassoon, M. and Lindow, V. (1995) 'Consulting and empowering Black service users', in S. Fernando, *Mental health in a multiethnic society*, London: Routledge.

147 Watters (1996, p 387) citing Sassons and Lindow (1995, p 103).

148 Rai-Atkins, A., Jama, A.A., Wright, N., Scott, V., Perring, C., Craig, G. and Katbamna, S. (2002) *Best practice in mental health: Advocacy for African, Caribbean and South Asian communities*, Bristol: The Policy Press.

149 Christie, Y. and Hill, N. (2003) *Black Spaces Project*, London: Mental Health Foundation.

150 Chouhan, K. and MacAttram, M. (2005) *Towards a blueprint for action: Building capacity in the black and minority ethnic voluntary and community sector providing mental health services*, London: Greater London Authority.

151 Platzer, H. and Foley, R. (2004) *Mental health advocacy in London: A mapping report*, London: London Development Centre.

152 Barnes, D. and Tate, A. (2000) *Advocacy from the outside inside: A review of the patients' advocacy service at Ashworth Hospital*, University of Durham/Ashworth Hospital Authority/North West Region NHS Secure Commissioning Team.

153 McKeown, M., Bingley, W. and Denoual, I. (2002) *A review of mental health advocacy services at the Edenfield Regional Secure Unit and Bowness High Dependency Unit, Prestwich Hospital*, Preston: UCLAN/North West Secure Commissioning Team.

154 Coleman, C. and Dunmur, J. (2000) *Surveying mental health advocacy needs in Sheffield*, Sheffield: Sheffield Community Health Council.

155 Platzer, H. and Foley, R. (2004) *Mental health advocacy in London: A mapping report*, London: London Development Centre.

156 Watters, C. (1996) 'Inequalities in mental health: the inner city mental health project', *Journal of Community & Applied Social Psychology*, vol 6, pp 383-394.

157 Christie, Y. and Hill, N. (2003) *Black Spaces Project*, London: Mental Health Foundation.

158 Christie, Y. and Hill, N. (2003) *Black Spaces Project*, London: Mental Health Foundation.

159 Rai-Atkins, A., Jama, A.A., Wright, N., Scott, V., Perring, C., Craig, G. and Katbamna, S. (2002) *Best practice in mental health: Advocacy for African, Caribbean and South Asian communities*, Bristol: The Policy Press.

160 McKeown, M., Bingley, W. and Denoual, I. (2002) *A review of mental health advocacy services at the Edenfield Regional Secure Unit and Bowness High Dependency Unit, Prestwich Hospital*, Preston: UCLAN/North West Secure Commissioning Team.

161 Mind (2006) *With us in mind: Service user recommendations for advocacy standards in England*, London: Mind.

162 Christie, Y. and Hill, N. (2003) *Black Spaces Project*, London: Mental Health Foundation.

163 Watters, C. (1996) 'Inequalities in mental health: the inner city mental health project', *Journal of Community & Applied Social Psychology*, vol 6, pp 383-394.

164 Chouhan, K. and MacAttram, M. (2005) *Towards a blueprint for action: Building capacity in the black and minority ethnic voluntary and community sector providing mental health services*, London: Greater London Authority.

165 Rai-Atkins, A., Jama, A.A., Wright, N., Scott, V., Perring, C., Craig, G. and Katbamna, S. (2002) *Best practice in mental health: Advocacy for African, Caribbean and South Asian communities*, Bristol: The Policy Press.

166 Keating, F., Robertson, D., McCulloch, A. and Francis, E. (2002) *Breaking the circles of fear: A review of the relationship between mental health services and African and Caribbean communities*, London: SCMH.

167 Platzer, H. and Foley, R. (2004) *Mental health advocacy in London: A mapping report*, London: London Development Centre.

168 Chouhan, K. and MacAttram, M. (2005) *Towards a blueprint for action: Building capacity in the black and minority ethnic voluntary and community sector providing mental health services*, London: Greater London Authority.

169 Chouhan, K. and MacAttram, M. (2005) *Towards a blueprint for action: Building capacity in the black and minority ethnic voluntary and community sector providing mental health services*, London: Greater London Authority.

170 Chouhan, K. and MacAttram, M. (2005) *Towards a blueprint for action: Building capacity in the black and minority ethnic voluntary and community sector providing mental health services*, London: Greater London Authority.

171 Watters, C. (1996) 'Inequalities in mental health: the inner city mental health project', *Journal of Community & Applied Social Psychology*, vol 6, pp 383-394.

172 Christie, Y. and Hill, N. (2003) *Black Spaces Project*, London: Mental Health Foundation.

173 Rai-Atkins, A., Jama, A.A., Wright, N., Scott, V., Perring, C., Craig, G. and Katbamna, S. (2002) *Best practice in mental health: Advocacy for African, Caribbean and South Asian communities*, Bristol: The Policy Press.

174 Platzer, H. and Foley, R. (2004) *Mental health advocacy in London: A mapping report*, London: London Development Centre.

175 McKeown, M., Bingley, W. and Denoual, I. (2002) *A review of mental health advocacy services at the Edenfield Regional Secure Unit and Bowness High Dependency Unit, Prestwich Hospital*, Preston: UCLAN/North West Secure Commissioning Team.

176 Platzer, H. and Foley, R. (2004) *Mental health advocacy in London: A mapping report*, London: London Development Centre.

177 ACMHS-Manchester (African Caribbean Mental Health Service) (2005) Information pack.

178 Family Health Isis, C.L. (2004) *Annual report/project description*.

179 Bromley Advocacy Project (2006) *Annual report 2005-2006*.

180 Brent Advocacy Concerns (2005) *Annual general report*, London: BAC.

181 Northern Ireland Association for Mental Health (2007) *Advocacy leaflet*, Belfast: Northern Ireland Association for Mental Health.

182 Trivedi, P., Bradford, R., Douglas, A., Elson, G., Falconer, L., Maule, M., Prophet, C., Sowu, K. and Thomas, P. (2002) 'Let the tiger roar...', *Mental Health Today*, pp 30-3.

183 Keating, F., Robertson, D., McCulloch, A. and Francis, E. (2002) *Breaking the circles of fear: A review of the relationship between mental health services and African and Caribbean communities*, London: SCMH.

184 Secker, J. and Harding, C. (2002) 'Users' perceptions of an African and Caribbean mental health resource centre', *Health and Social Care in the Community*, vol 10, pp 270-6.

185 Myers, L.J. (1993) *Understanding an Afrocentric world view: Introduction to an optimal psychology* (2nd edn), Iowa: Kendall/ Hunt Publishing Company, cited by M. Phillips (1997) 'Ipamo: an alternative to hospital for the African and Caribbean communities in Lambeth', *Mental Health Review*, vol 2, no 1, pp 18-21.

186 Platzer, H. and Foley, R. (2004) *Mental health advocacy in London: A mapping report*, London: London Development Centre.

187 Roseman, S., Korten, A. and Newman, L. (2000) 'Efficacy of continuing advocacy in involuntary treatment', *Psychiatric Services*, vol 51, no 8, pp 1029-33.

188 Rai-Atkins, A., Jama, A.A., Wright, N., Scott, V., Perring, C., Craig, G. and Katbamna, S. (2002) *Best practice in mental health: Advocacy for African, Caribbean and South Asian communities*, Bristol: The Policy Press.

189 Mind (2006) *With us in mind: Service user recommendations for advocacy standards in England*, London: Mind.

190 Bowes, A. and Sim, D. (2006) 'Advocacy for Black and minority ethnic communities: understandings and expectations', *British Journal of Social Work*.
see also Bowes, A.M., Valenti, M., Sim, D. and Macintosh, S. (2002) *Delivering advocacy services to Glasgow's Black and minority ethnic communities: Report to Glasgow City Council and Greater Glasgow Health Board*, Department of Applied Social Science, University of Stirling and Greater Glasgow Health Board.

191 Ludwig, A. (2001) 'Access to advocacy', *Diverse Minds Magazine*, Issue 10, October, pp 12-13.

192 Barker, I., Newbigging, K. and Peck, E. (1997) 'Characteristics for sustained advocacy projects in mental health services', *Community Care Management & Planning Review*, vol 4, August, pp 132-8.

193 Griffiths, S. (2003) 'Developing an evaluation framework: the Mellow experience', *Journal of Mental Health Promotion*, vol 2, no 2, pp 22-8.

194 Rapaport, J., Manthorpe, J., Moriarty, J., Hussein, S. and Collins, J. (2005) 'Advocacy and people with learning disabilities in the UK', Journal of Intellectual Disabilities, vol 9, no 4, pp 2999-319.

195 Ritchie, J. and Lewis, J. (2003) *Qualitative research practice: A guide for social science students and researchers*, London: Sage Publications.

196 Department of Health (2006) *Reward and recognition: The principles and practice of service user payments and reimbursement in health and social* care, London: DH.

197 Bowling, A. (2002) *Research methods in health*, Maidenhead: Open University Press.

198 Spencer, L., Ritchie, J., Lewis, J. and Dillon, L. (2003) *Quality in qualitative evaluation: Government Chief Social Researcher's Office*, London: Cabinet Office.

199 McKeown, M., Bingley, W. and Denoual, I. (2002) *A review of mental health advocacy services at the Edenfield Regional Secure Unit and Bowness High Dependency Unit, Prestwich Hospital*, Preston: UCLAN/North West Secure Commissioning Team.

200 Keating, F., Robertson, D., McCulloch, A. and Francis, E. (2002) *Breaking the circles of fear: A review of the relationship between mental health services and African and Caribbean communities*, London: SCMH.

201 Carvalho, C. (2003) 'Advocacy for all?', *Planet Advocacy*, June, pp 3-5.

202 Healthcare Commission, Mental Health Act Commission and National Institute for Mental Health in England (2005) *Count me in: Results of a national census of inpatients in mental health hospitals and facilities in England and Wales*, London: Healthcare Commission.

203 Barnes, D., Brandon, T. and Webb, T. (2002) *Independent specialist advocacy in England and Wales: Recommendations for good practice*, Durham: University of Durham.

204 Department of Health (2005) *Delivering race equality in mental health care: An action plan for reform inside and outside services*, London: The Stationery Office.

205 See also National Institute for Mental Health in England (2003) *Inside outside Improving mental health services for Black and minority ethnic communities in England*, London: NIMHE.

Department of Health (2003) *Engaging and changing: Developing effective policy for the care and treatment of Black and minority ethnic detained patients*, London: National Institute for Mental Health, England, UCLAN and Mental Health Act Commission.

206 Fernando, S. (2007) 'From "whole systems change" to no change', *Openmind*, vol 143, January/February, p 25.

207 Christie, Y. and Hill, N. (2003) *Black Spaces Project*, London: Mental Health Foundation.

208 Chouhan, K. and MacAttram, M. (2005) *Towards a blueprint for action: Building capacity in the black and minority ethnic voluntary and community sector providing mental health services*, London: Greater London Authority.

209 Healthcare Commission, Mental Health Act Commission and National Institute for Mental Health in England (2005) *Count me in: Results of a national census of inpatients in mental health hospitals and facilities in England and Wales*, London: Healthcare Commission.

210 Bowes, A.M., Valenti, M., Sim, D. and Macintosh, S. (2002) *Delivering advocacy services to Glasgow's Black and minority ethnic communities: Report to Glasgow City Council and Greater Glasgow Health Board*, Department of Applied Social Science, University of Stirling and Greater Glasgow Health Board.

211 Winters, M. and Patel, K. (2003) *The Department of Health's Black and minority ethnic drug misuse needs assessment project, Report 1: The process*, Preston: Centre for Ethnicity and Health, University of Central Lancashire.

212 Olajide, D. (1999) 'Government policy and ethnic minority mental health', in K. Bhui and D. Olajide (eds) *Mental health provision for a multicultural society*, London: Saunders.

213 Keating, F., Robertson, D., McCulloch, A. and Francis, E. (2002) *Breaking the circles of fear: A review of the relationship between mental health services and African and Caribbean communities*, London: SCMH.

African and Caribbean Mental Health Services
Zion Community Resource Centre
339 Stretford Road
Hulme
Manchester M15 4ZY
Tel: 0161 226 9562
Email: admin@acmhs-blackmentalhealth.org.uk

The African and Caribbean Mental Health Services (ACMHS) is a voluntary charitable organisation that provides support to African and African Caribbean (AC) people with mental health problems who are aged between 18 and 65 years and living in the Manchester and Trafford areas.

ACMHS was formed in October 1989 as a direct result of concern expressed in the community about the frequency with which second-generation African and African and Caribbean youths were admitted to psychiatric hospitals and the regional forensic unit. Services provided include support, casework, advocacy, that is, welfare rights, benefits, attending ward rounds and tribunals, counselling, employment/education and training advice and support to prisoners in Manchester. Drop-in services are available four days a week involving sport, music, art and socialising.

ACMHS has recently re-established a primary care mental health team working with people aged 16-65 living in Manchester and who have common mental health problems, that is, depression, anxiety, relationship problems and low self-esteem. The primary care workers offer brief interventions that focus mainly on current problems and help people develop techniques to manage their problems better.

Equalities: the National Council for Disabled People and Carers from Black and Minority Ethnic Communities
(Equalities: Disabled People including those with learning disabilities, mental health, multiple impairments, sensory and visual disabilities, as well as those with long-term conditions)

Waltham Forest College
Forest Road
London E17 4JB
Tel: 020 85273211
Advocacy Line: 020 8527 3712
Fax: 0208 418 5662
www.encweb.org.uk
Email: enquiries@equalitiesnational.org.uk

Equalities is a national independent enterprise run by its service users, who all have a good understanding of the barriers disabled people and carers from our communities experience when trying to get the help and support we feel we are in need of. In order to gain access to services that are more inclusive and culturally sensitive to the needs of disabled people and carers from Black and minority ethnic (BME) communities, Equalities are striving to keep the issues identified elevated on a national platform structured regionally but from the voices at a local grass-roots and community level where the concerns and issues of these groups receive the same recognition as all disabled people, and *from* the *direct voices* of BME disabled people and carers. We are currently forming our National Networks of Enterprises, the National Community Outreach Advocacy programme, and service user involvement/participation, training and leadership programmes across the 8/9 regions. We are without any doubt unique in our delivery and want to continue working to change a culture rooted in the narrow-minded way in which service provision is delivered to us. We aim to deliver innovative services and expect the same from other service providers.

The aims and objectives of Equalities are:

• to empower all service recipients of Equalities, enabling easier access to services and therefore the enhancement of life;

- to promote, through empowerment, the independence of disabled people and their families, supporting them to express what their needs are at all times, participating during assessment, referral and correspondence processes;
- to continuously play an active role in campaigning for the rights of all disabled people, especially those from BME communities/groups who are often under-represented as service recipients, and participatory communities, and whose views are also often under-represented;
- to welcome the referrals of people who may not class themselves as having a disability due to fear of stigma, Share the concepts of Independent Living, and the social model and how that reflects within their lives;
- to share information and keep members up to date on new policies, consultations, forums and meetings of interest;
- to train service users and carers to become community outreach advocates.

Lancashire Advocacy
Howick House
Howick Park Avenue
Penwortham
Preston PR2 5AL
Tel: 01772 744050

Lancashire Advocacy is a user-led charity that works collaboratively with advocacy projects, service users and voluntary organisations to enhance the provision of advocacy and to promote service user involvement in health and social services. Over the past 14 years the organisation has been instrumental in developing eight short-term generic advocacy projects, which are all now autonomous organisations. Lancashire Advocacy has also developed new and innovative projects including a Lancashire-wide self-advocacy group and a new dementia-focused advocacy project.

Lancashire Advocacy has worked hard to develop a proven track record of being an effective provider of services to the advocacy and service user communities. Through its hard work, it has accumulated expertise, and built strong tangible relationships with individuals, advocacy projects, voluntary organisations, academics, providers, purchasers and commissioners. The development of Lancashire Advocacy has always been led by the needs of its service users and a commitment to develop services to meet advocacy and service user gaps in Lancashire.

Lancashire Advocacy currently employs eight members of staff and supports over 120 volunteers from the groups, which are facilitated by Lancashire Advocacy. Lancashire Advocacy also hosts several other self-organised user groups including Preston Mental Health Service User Forum, GEM (Giving Experience Meaning), a user-led training group, Preston People First and Lancashire Self-Advocacy project.

Lancashire Advocacy is really well networked and respected among the local and national advocacy community and has collected an extensive resource library of advocacy texts, including a large collection of grey material such as reports produced by other advocacy organisations. Lancashire Advocacy was instrumental in developing Lancashire-wide standards for best practice in advocacy, including advice to advocacy projects to develop best practice protocols for engaging BME communities and service users.

Lancashire Advocacy and its hosted groups have a long-standing relationship with the University of Central Lancashire (UCLAN), including involvement in the setting up and management of the advocacy course, other contributions to user involvement at the university including significant involvement in the Comensus project.

Appendix 2
Key reports and policy initiatives*

Year	Report/policy initiative	Focus	Main implications
1994	DH: Mental Health Task Force	Report on London project and regional race programmes	Demonstrated dissatisfaction with services and highlighted good practice
1994	Black mental health: A dialogue for change	Integration of integrating voluntary and statutory sector practice	Acknowledging and promoting the value of the voluntary sector for Black communities
1994	Department of Health EL (94) 77	NHE executive letter instructing all service providers to collect data on service user's ethnic origins	Disaggregation of data on ethnicity will provide a basis for considering whether the needs of different ethnic groups are being adequately considered
1995	Learning the lessons: Zito Trust	Review of all the homicide inquiries by someone with a mental illness	Emphasised role of race and ethnicity of people with a mental illness and service shortfalls for BME communities
1995	DH: Mental health: Towards a better understanding	Health of the Nation information booklet for BME individuals with a mental illness and their carers	Highlighted the position of carers and their needs

Appendix 2 continued

Year	Report/policy initiative	Focus	Main implications
1998/ 99	DH: A first class service	Advocated National Service Frameworks that set standards of care to improve quality and access	Set out action to address inequalities in care
1999	Stephen Lawrence report	Inquiry into the murder of Stephen Lawrence, which highlighted institutional racism in the failure of the criminal justice system to bring murderers to justice	The NHS and other public bodies expected to examine structures and services in the light of the report in order to tackle institutional racism
1999	DH: National Service Framework for mental health	Describes seven standards to improve the quality of and access to mental health services	Emphasised the cultural sensitivity of services for African and Caribbean communities

Appendix 2 continued

Year	Report/policy initiative	Focus	Main implications
2000	SCMH: A visit by the Mental Health Act Commission to 104 mental health and learning disability units in England and Wales – improving care for detained patients from BME communities	Report of a visit (Visit 2) in 1999 by the Mental Health Act Commission and the SCMH on care for detained patients from BME communities	Highlighted that many detained patients from BME communities were not receiving care sensitive to their cultural backgrounds; that many services collected ethnic data but did not use the information to improve services and that three quarters of units had no policies for dealing with racial harassment
2000	DH: The NHS Plan	A key aim is to address inequalities in health	Framework for performance management
2002	The Race Relations (Amendment) Act	Places a general duty on public authorities to eliminate unlawful discrimination and promote equality of opportunity between different ethnic groups	Places the responsibility to take action on organisations rather than leaving it up to individuals. Public authorities required to undertake race impact assessments of policies and major changes in service provision to establish whether unlawful discrimination is taking place

Appendix 2 continued

Year	Report/policy initiative	Focus	Main implications
2002	SCMH: Breaking the circles of fear	A review of the relationship between mental health services and African and Caribbean communities	Identified factors that impact negatively on the engagement of Black people with services and vice versa. Coined the term *circles of fear* to describe the experience of mental health services and racism, which interact to shape the poor engagement with services and disproportionate rates of admission and compulsory detention
2002	NIMHE: Inside outside	Guidance to improve mental health services for BME communities in England	The introduction of CDWs to engage with and build the capacity of BME communities
2003	NIMHE: Engaging and changing	Report commissioned following National Visit 2 by Mental Health Act Commission, to provide guidance in relation to policies concerning the care and treatment of BME detained patients in the context of the Race Relations Act	Advocates the importance of community engagement as a method for facilitating organisational change. Based on community engagement work in substance misuse and BME communities developed in Centre for Ethnicity and Health at UCLAN

Appendix 2 continued

Year	Report/policy initiative	Focus	Main implications
2003	Blofeld report on the independent inquiry into the death of David Bennett published by Norfolk, Suffolk and Cambridgeshire Strategic Health Authority	David (Rocky) Bennett was a 38-year-old African and Caribbean man, diagnosed with schizophrenia while under the care of Norfolk Mental Health Care NHS Trust. He died while being restrained in a medium secure unit	Adopted the definition of institutional racism from the Macpherson inquiry and recommended that ministers should acknowledge its existence and make a commitment to eliminate it. Supported and recommended the development of the BME and mental health strategy
2003	Social Exclusion Unit report on mental health	Sets out an action plan to address the stigma, discrimination and social exclusion faced by adults with mental health problems	Confirmed the role that the voluntary and community sector play in mental health service provision, particularly for people less likely to access statutory services. Also highlighted the importance of community participation and the importance of social networks
2004	DH: 10-point action plan to promote race equality in the NHS	Outlines 10 areas of action for the NHS and DH to give greater prominence to race equality and adopt a strategic approach to tackling inequalities	Independent panel is keeping the plan under review, providing advice and challenging progress on it

Appendix 2 continued

Year	Report/policy initiative	Focus	Main implications
2005	DH: Delivering race equality in mental health care	A strategy to improve mental health provision to BME communities incorporating the government's response to the independent inquiry into the death of David Bennett	Identified outcomes for people from BME communities in contact with mental health services. Identified provision of appropriate advocacy for BME communities as a key action for PCTs
2005	Healthcare Commission: Count me in	National census of in-patients in mental health hospitals and facilities in England and Wales	Highlights disproportionate rates of admission to psychiatric hospitals and detention under the Mental Health Act for Black African, Black Caribbean and Black Other
2006	Welsh Assembly: Raising the standard: Race equality action plan for adult mental health services in Wales	An action plan to improve equality of access, equality of treatment and equality of outcomes for different minority ethnic groups in Wales	Trusts, local health boards and local authorities required to submit plan to the government detailing how they will deliver the action plan locally. This includes action in relation to collecting evidence, training staff, delivery of services and service monitoring and evaluation

Appendix 2 continued

Year	Report/policy initiative	Focus	Main implications
2007	Healthcare Commission: Count me in	Results of the 2006 national census of in-patients in mental health and learning disability services in England and Wales	Points to different patterns of admission and detention for different ethnic groups. Confirmed rates of detention higher in Black and White/Black mixed groups

Notes: DH: Department of Health; SCMH: Sainsbury Centre for Mental Health; BME: Black and minority ethnic; African and Caribbean: African and Caribbean; NIMHE: National Institute for Mental Health in England; CDW: community development worker; UCLAN: University of Central Lancashire; PCT: primary care trust

---

* Adapted and updated from Olajide[212] in Keating et al.[213]

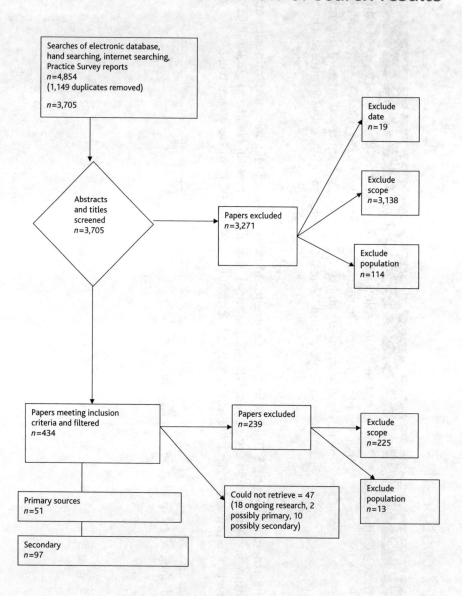

Appendix 4
Typology of mental health advocacy provision for African and Caribbean men

Focus	Type of organisation	Number
African and Caribbean (African and Caribbean)-focused	African and Caribbean mental health advocacy	7
	African and Caribbean mental health service	17
	African and Caribbean service user group	5
	African and Caribbean community associations	58
Back and minority ethnic (BME) community-focused	BME mental health advocacy	6
	BME mental health service	14
	BME user group	1
	BME community	10
Advocacy-focused	Generic advocacy	82
	User group	6
	Mental health advocacy	185
	Total	**391**
Other	Capacity building	15

Appendix 5
Types of advocacy

Characteristics	Citizen	Self	Peer	Professional/specialist	Legal/representation	Community	Collective/group	Non-instructed
Definition	A citizen from the community supports an individual and represents their wishes	The individual expresses and represents their own views	Someone with experience of using mental health services supports and speaks on behalf of someone else	Trained and paid advocates who provide a service to protect an individual's rights through information, assistance and representation	Representation of an individual's wishes during a legal process e.g. MHRT or formal complaint	A community represents their views in order to protect and enhance the status of community members	People with similar experiences represent their shared views on behalf of the group. User groups and patient councils are an example.	Representation of wishes on behalf of a person unable to express them, usually because of lack of capacity

Appendix 5 continued

Characteristics	Citizen	Self	Peer	Professional/specialist	Legal/representation	Community	Collective/group	Non-instructed
Paid/unpaid	Unpaid Paid co-ordinator	Unpaid		Paid	Paid	Unpaid	Unpaid	Paid
Individual/group	Individual	Individual	Individual	Individual	Individual	Group	Group	Individual

Appendix 5 continued

Characteristics	Citizen	Self	Peer	Professional/ specialist	Legal/repre- sentation	Commu- nity	Collec- tive/ group	Non-in- structed
Similar/ different (gender, shared heritage, experience of mental health issues, service user etc)	Similar. Matches people with partners from the same community. May not have experience of mental health issues.	Identical	Similar	Likely to be different in terms of gender and heritage although may be an ex-or current service user	Different	Similar	Similar	Likely to be different

Appendix 5 continued

Characteristics	Citizen	Self	Peer	Professional/specialist	Legal/representation	Community	Collective/group	Non-instructed
Proactive/reactive	Proactive and reactive	Reactive	Reactive	Reactive	Reactive	Proactive and reactive	Proactive and reactive	Reactive
Trained/untrained	Untrained	Maybe support and/or training available to build confidence and skills	Maybe support and/or training available to build confidence and skills	Sometimes trained	Trained	Untrained	Maybe support and/or training available to build confidence and skills	Sometimes trained
Independence/Related to services	Independent	Independent	Independent	Independent	Independent	Community may also provide mental health services	Independent	Independent

Appendix 5 continued

Character-istics	Citizen	Self	Peer	Professional/specialist	Legal/rep-resenta-tion	Com-munity	Collec-tive/group	Non-in-struct-ed
Short-term/long-term	Long-term	Long-term	Long-term	Short-term	Short-term	Long-term	Long-term	Short-term
Community participation	Supports person to take fuller role in the community	Focused on relationship with mental health services	Focused on relationship with mental health services	Focused on relationship with mental health services	Focused on relationship with mental health services	Supports person to take fuller role in the community	Focused on relationship with mental health services	Focused on relationship with mental health services

Appendix 6
Description of types of organisational arrangements

Type of organisation		Organisation	Functions	Staffing	Advocacy provision
African and/ or African Caribbean (African and Caribbean)- focused	African and Caribbean groups	Often constituted around single national or ethnic group	Largely concerned with support for immigrants – information, advice giving (bilingual), help in navigating bureaucracies, general support and signposting to other services. Anyone with mental health difficulties is dealt with in this way, with little direct support for mental health, but do not rule this out	Small numbers of paid staff (two or less) often staffed by volunteers	Mission is not necessarily articulated as advocacy, but work does have recognisable advocacy strands and often involves accompanying people to GP appointments and, if necessary, supporting people to get their point of view across

Appendix 6 continued

Type of organisation	Organisation	Functions	Staffing	Advocacy provision
African and Caribbean community welfare and social groups	Membership organisations	Raise funds for local charities, organise social and cultural events in community. Mutual support and solidarity networks, including supporting people with mental health issues, but is not the main focus. Systems of home visiting, organised by regular volunteers, or more simply in terms of members looking out for each other. Some of these groups have premises others do not. Might offer health seminars and provision of health and welfare advice, and issues relating to African and Caribbean people. Some members have background in health services and are well placed to offer advice. Some members are in families who have a relative with severe mental illness (smi)	Very much a voluntary enterprise, little evidence of paid staff	Providing information and signposting to services

Appendix 6 continued

Type of organisation	Organisation	Functions	Staffing	Advocacy provision
African and Caribbean mental health advocacy	Stand-alone or more usually organised within a larger umbrella organisation, offering alternative care services. Rarely may be part of a generic mental advocacy service	Culturally specific service, formal, professional model of advocacy. Sometimes targets broad health issues, sometimes focused explicitly on mental health	Those organisations that are just constituted for advocacy for African and Caribbean community tend to be small, employing one to three advocates, often part time	Culturally specific advocacy

Appendix 6 continued

Type of organisation	Organisation	Functions	Staffing	Advocac provision
African and Caribbean mental health services	Culturally specific services as an alternative to parts of the mainstream NHS. Often run in parallel or adjunct with cross-referrals. Often based on social model of care rather than medical model	Alternative culturally specific services. Provide a range of direct services, including housing, group work and counselling. Often provide advocacy as an integral function	Some of these organisations are quite large, with one employing 32 staff in total across a range of organisations. One was small enough to employ just four staff	Can refer to support rather than advocacy, although some of the bigger services have discrete advocacy wings. All staff engaged in advocacy as part of their role

Appendix 6 continued

Type of organisation	Organisation	Functions	Staffing	Advocay provision
Black and minority ethnic (BME) organisa-tions	Multicultural groups	Similar to African and African and Caribbean social and welfare groups	A range of social and welfare activities	Largely supported by volunteers, one had two staff	Not main focus but may include recognisable advocacy functions
	African and African and Caribbean and/or BME umbrella organisa-tions	Host a number of different groups or services. May be a central coordinating group supporting other organisations	Capacity building and/or coordinating function. May also represent other groups	Vary in size – one large grouping was found, employing 68 staff across all organisations	May include support for fledgling advocacy groups, but does not involve direct provision of advocacy

Appendix 6 continued

Type of organisation	Organisation	Functions	Staffing	Advocacy provision
BME advocacy organisations	Stand-alone or part of organisation offering alternative care services	Providing culturally sensitive advocacy for a range of BME groups. Sometimes these groups have other wings/dual roles, sometimes staffed separately, doing things like carer support, befriending, or user development workers	Typically employ three to four staff	Culturally sensitive advocacy
BME mental health services	Maybe established within the NHS or social services or independent	Alternative services or culturally sensitive services. Some provide direct services; others exist to work alongside established caseworkers to improve the cultural sensitivity of their work	Staffing levels range from two to six, typically with no more than one individual focused on African and Caribbean clients	Culturally sensitive advocacy

Appendix 6 continued

Type of organisation		Organisation	Functions	Staffing	Advocacy provision
Advocacy	Generic advocacy services	Providing advocacy across a range of client groups including mental health. Varies and may include volunteers	Tends to be independent professional advocacy. Also citizen advocacy of service is also for people with learning difficulties. Collective and peer advocacy also provided but much less frequently than individual casework	Vary	May have developed to ensure cultural sensitivity but rare and the extent of this will reflect the local demography and existence of other advocacy providers
	Generic mental health advocacy services	Providing mental health advocacy in different settings	Tends to be independent professional advocacy. May also be collective, self and peer advocacy but much less frequently than individual casework	Varies and may include volunteers	As above

1 African and Caribbean-focused service

This service aims to provide a culturally sensitive advocacy service to African and Caribbean people experiencing mental distress in a defined geographical area. It defines advocacy as 'helping people put their views across and primarily support people to speak up for themselves'. The advocacy service was provided as part of a range of social, therapeutic and specialist mental health services for African and Caribbean communities.

There was one full-time member of staff, line-managed by a manger from a mainstream advocacy service. The service used to have volunteers but the advocate did not have enough capacity to recruit and train them. The service was funded by the primary care trust (PCT) on an annual basis and required to deliver against targets related to advocacy provision in hospital settings. It had also provided advocacy with men in prison and secure settings. However, it lost its funding for advocacy and a board member continues to provide advocacy in a voluntary capacity.

All of the clients using the service are from African and Caribbean communities with usually equal proportions of men and women using the service.

The service identified medication, leave arrangements, Section 136, police involvement, cultural interpretation of statutory and professional services and over-representation in mental health services as major issues for the men using the service. It aims to address these issues as well as over-medication, prolonged detention and stigmatisation of African and Caribbean men. The service went on to identify suspicion and mistrust and the need to have a clear and separate identity from mainstream services in order to engage successfully with men as a the major barrier. The lack of capacity and the limitations that this imposes in terms of choice of advocate was also cited as a significant barrier.

The need to provide advocates not from the same community, because of concerns about confidentiality, was highlighted as an area for future service development.

In terms of preferred organisational arrangements, the service was keen to reinstate funding for its advocacy service. It suggested that statutory services should be required to consider the provision of gender-specific and culturally specific services – an ambition consistent with the current legislative framework for equalities.

2   Black and minority ethnic (BME)-focused service

This service aims to support and empower users to not only access services, but also more importantly to enhance their well-being and gain confidence to improve their circumstances. It defines advocacy 'as an individual being supported in his goal and being understood'. The service covers a broad range of people from BME communities with disabilities and their carers, including those experiencing mental health problems.

There is one full-time member of staff, two part-time, six volunteers, two professional advisers in a voluntary capacity and social work student learners. The service has no core long-term funding and supports its advocacy activity through presentations, consultancy and project work. Advocacy is integral to the organisation and it has a support programme so that service users are also trainee advocates and also volunteers.

African and Caribbean men make up 50% of the clients. The service defined the advocacy needs of these men in terms of effective communication, multiple discrimination, over-representation in the mental health and criminal justice system, a failure of services to meet holistic needs and stereotyping, raising concerns about the needs of Black men going unmet and being overlooked. It identified the challenges in meeting these needs in terms of racism and a widespread lack of awareness of the human rights agenda. It aims to address these by not giving up on their client.

Areas for service development relate to securing funding and the preferred arrangements for advocacy for African and Caribbean men are described in terms of a networking, mentoring and regeneration programme.

The organisation is relatively unique in being user-led and this is reflected throughout with an emphasis on supporting progression from being a service user to an advocate.

3   Generic mental health advocacy service

3.1   Little capacity to provide a culturally appropriate response for African and Caribbean men

3.1.1   Low population of African and Caribbean men

This service defines advocacy as 'a confidential service, working for you, working with you' and the role of the advocate being 'to represent the views and the rights of the client. This can be done through supporting people to express their views and concerns, access information and services, defend and promote their rights and responsibilities, explore choices and options'.

The service is part of a project that also deals with welfare benefits and debt. The project is commissioned by service users and funded through the lottery. There are one-and-a-half whole time equivalent and a social work student on placement most of the time. The service covers both in-patient and community settings but the person must be using specialist mental health services.

It is located in an area that covers both rural and urban areas that has a very low demographic profile of African and Caribbean communities and not surprisingly has only provided a service to one man. It did not identify any preference for organisational arrangements given the very low numbers of African and Caribbean people living locally.

This is another example of a service user-led organisation and this is reflected throughout the organisation.

3.1.2   Moderate population of African and Caribbean men

The services defines advocacy as 'taking action to help people say what they want, secure their rights, represent their interests and obtain the services they need'. It frames advocacy in terms of social inclusion, equality and social justice.

The service is a charity and is funded through several PCTs, as it covers a relatively large area. The population of African and Caribbean men in these areas varies significantly with relatively few living in the more rural area and significant populations in the urban areas. The service has seven whole time equivalents and no volunteers.

The service has little contact with African and Caribbean men and was unable to identify how many men it had seen in the past year, and thought that it was a very small percentage, possibly none.

There appears to be a well-developed training strategy but there has been no specific training undertaken on the needs of these communities and how advocacy providers can respond to this. The service called for a cultural shift in both statutory and not-for-profit sectors in order to improve the response to African and Caribbean men and identified developing a comprehensive understanding of the economic, social and cultural background of the men as the major challenge in meeting their advocacy needs.

The expressed preference for organisational arrangements was for a generic service, with advocates receiving special training and delivery supported by partnerships with specialist BME mental health services.

3.2 With capacity to provide a culturally appropriate response

This service provides independent mental health advocacy with people experiencing mental distress including dementia and also aims to enable involvement in the development of appropriate services. The service defines advocacy as 'speaking on behalf of someone and supporting someone to speak up for themselves'. There is open referral, aiming to have the majority as self-referrals.

The service has six-and-a-half whole time equivalents with two part-time staff providing advocacy specifically for people from BME communities, one being an Asian advocate and one African and Caribbean. The service used to have volunteers but they did not provide a good return on the investment of time needed to support them. The service is mainly funded by social services and the PCT, usually on a three-year basis and there is a service-level agreement describing advocacy services to be provided, quality standards for the service and the monitoring arrangements. The current funding is for 12 months because of PCT configuration.

The service stressed the importance of having advocates from the same or similar ethnic background and since the appointment of the two BME advocates the percentage of people from BME communities has increased from 8% to 18% over a five-year period. The major challenges highlighted in meeting the needs of African and Caribbean men were stigma, a lack of trust so that help was not sought, experience of greater restrictions and more problems with side-effects of medication, difficulties in relation to benefits and debt and isolation and lack of family networks for older people.

Service user involvement is significant and the management group has to be chaired by a service user and aims for 50% service user representation. There has been an investment in training.

4   A generic advocacy service

This service provides advocacy for disabled people including mental health service users. They define advocacy as 'taking action to help people say what they want and to secure their rights'.

The service is provided by five paid workers, including two part-time and 65 volunteers. Funding comes from a variety of sources, including the local authority and a variety of charitable trusts with most only secured for 12 months. They receive referrals from a range of sources including friends, family and self-referral.

The service is well used by African and Caribbean men who make up 20% of the current advocacy partners. The service is in the process of recruiting a BME advocacy worker to increase the cultural sensitivity of the service. They identified housing, the quality of mental healthcare, providing a range of options and difficulties accessing interpreters as needed as the major challenges in meeting the needs of African and Caribbean men.

The service has adopted the advocacy charter and has developed a set of advocacy standards for BME groups. Service user involvement is well developed.

Index